D1287826

THE MALE HORMONE

Books by Paul de Kruif

THE MALE HORMONE

by
Paul de Kruif

"Remember, Paul, people are very open-minded about new things—so long as they're exactly like the old ones."
CHARLES F. KETTERING

NEW YORK
HARCOURT, BRACE AND COMPANY

A WARTIME BOOK

PRINTED IN THE UNITED STATES OF AMERICA

ACKNOWLEDGMENTS

THE many months of research in preparation for the writing of this adventure of the male hormone were made possible by Mr. De Witt Wallace. His confidence in the results of that investigation led to an article in *The Reader's Digest,* entitled "Can Man's Prime Be Prolonged?" That was the framework upon which this book has been built. To Mr. Wallace for his boldness in presenting so delicate a subject to millions of people, my thanks and admiration.

To Kenneth W. Payne, William Hard, Jr., and Henry Morton Robinson, all of *The Reader's Digest* staff, all my gratitude for their skill in guiding me through the tough job of making the astounding facts regarding the male hormone credible to the millions.

I must thank Dr. Ralph D. Shaner for his generosity in placing his deep knowledge of the literature on the male hormone at my disposal and for his helping me in the assembly of the source materials of the book.

Finally to Mr. Andrew Salter, psychologist, my thanks for his devotion and skill in applying Pavlov's conditioned reflex technique to me, with the result of disinhibiting my mid-brain to such a degree that it was possible to write the adventure of the male hormone.

PAUL DE KRUIF

THIS BOOK IS AGAIN FOR
RHEA

CONTENTS

CONTENTS

PART 1

GROWING OLD ISN'T NATURAL

CHAPTER ONE

FIFTEEN years ago this Autumn I began writing a story about men against death that opened with the too obvious words, "I don't want to die." I was then thirty-nine years old and strong, swimming in Lake Michigan, like a slightly middle-aged walrus, vain of that strength, yet haunted by a scientific promise that it was not likely to be mine for many years longer. Warnings from the life tables showed that, getting the breaks of the average man, there were only twenty more years to live. It was far too short. There was so much left to learn before I could attain the beginning of wisdom, so much of my past life to atone for before I could hope to become a decent man. At the same time, a great deal of study had shown me that science had already done about as much as could be expected in delaying the aging of my muscles, brain, bones and arteries.

To tell the truth, medical science had been an absolute flop in its unorganized and feeble effort to check the dissolution and death that marched toward all middle-aged men and women. Men of science cut themselves splendid pieces of cake for their saving of babies, children and young people from many microbic deaths, but they had nothing to offer to push back the on-rushing disease of old age. It seemed as cruel as it was idiotic and wasteful. It seemed as if the young were preserved to a time of the beginning of wisdom and serene enjoyment of life, then to begin to crack up with the diseases of degeneration, then to be told by science, "We were only fooling you."

3

It was the bitter knowledge of the threat of this approaching degeneration that taunted me, lying awake in the dark when the northwest gales shook our little shack on the Lake Michigan shore in the Autumn of 1929.

Looking back now on this curious long-range fear of death, it is clear that this was more than a mere silly crossing of a bridge twenty years before I might expect to come to it. If I had been healthily optimistic, I'd only have been thinking of cheating that average, science or no science, and living strong, till eighty. This worry about living no longer than the average was very likely the first faint symptom of a sapping of what, for lack of a more precise scientific term, may be called my *"total vitality."*

I remember lying awake nights dreading the approach of my fortieth birthday.

In the daytime, to prove my virility to myself and to exhibit it to others, I indulged in excesses of surf-swimming in cold Lake Michigan and tried to be a miniature Paul Bunyan at cross-cut sawing and with the double-bitted Michigan axe. That year the big lake was on one of its high-water rampages, eroding great gobs of our dune at Blue Water, taking many beautiful beech and pine trees. In the daytimes that Autumn I was encouraged by our beach-master and forester, William Deplidge, who, God rest his bones, seemed never to be scared of anything including dying.

All of my life has been a not very bright learning from better men than I am, and William Deplidge will always be remembered as one of my best masters. He was already then very wizened, hardly more than one hundred pounds, and badly arthritic and nearing seventy; and every day, while we worked in the surf tearing at the base of our dune, Deplidge would shake his fist at the boiling surf of the big lake and say, "By God! We'll lick it!" Dog-tired at the end of the day, he'd give a cackling laugh and mumble, "By God, Paul, you and I will live to be a hundred."

His right arm was so crippled with arthritis that he used his left hand (through the steering wheel) to shift the gears of his Ford; he walked, drag-footed and like Charlie Chaplin; he had a splendid head of iron-gray hair and was fond of widows. Against Lake Michigan he had a great defiance and was indomitable, and we worked many months like beavers trying to rip-rap the vanishing beach with sandbags and saplings, cutting and lashing together thousands of saplings and shoving them down the steep bank and filling and lifting thousands of sandbags and smashing them down on the saplings to hold them fixed in the swirling surf. I was proud, one day, hearing old Deplidge remark about me, "He's a terror!"

It's clear now that this back-breaking physical activity and other less dignified excesses of the next two or three years were a sort of last kick of the dying mule of my youthful energy. After that, during the next ten years, this he-man activity was slowly but inexorably on the wane. My jogging four miles along the beach slowed down to a walk, ostensibly because my medical friends assured me running was bad for my heart muscle, but really because my legs couldn't take it the way they used to. Now three or four hours with the double-bitted axe and cross-cut saw were plenty. This earned sardonic praise by Deplidge, who himself was shrinking so you'd think a thirty mile an hour breeze from Lake Michigan would blow him away; he was well past seventy but still ready to work the full day as we'd done in 1929. He never worried about himself but only about his underdog farmer friends, eking their living on the thin land back of the sand dunes. He was Christ in miniature.

Toward fifty, I began to sweat too easily wood-cutting, even on the tangiest days of the Autumn; and I began to sleep more and more fitfully, waking up nights and scared, but of nothing. I drank more whiskey to counteract the tiredness and to chase away causeless fears and told myself that Johnnie Walker Black Label was the correct prescription, not only because it is expensive and tasty but because it relaxes the little arteries. Upon the advice of Dr. James S. McLester, I joined the Society for the Prevention of Coronary Occlusion (blocking of the heart arteries). The ritual of this informal society is a couple of dry Martinis before lunch on all possible occasions.

I had a little physical vanity left. I could still swim a fairly fast free-style for two miles in Lake Michigan but made excuses for not doing it so often. At the beginning of the nineteen-forties I had definitely become a walrus, emeritus.

There was at this time a final and most disturbing sign of the draining of my total vitality. Nothing could have kept me out of the first World War, though about its issues I was foggy. Now, hating the lies and the destructive nihilism of the Nazis, Fascists, and Japs, I did not offer to go to fight them. Let the younger fellows do the dying against the most evil menace mankind had ever known. I would stand on the sidelines, cheering.

CHAPTER TWO

It was Doctor Herman N. Bundesen, President of the Chicago Board of Health, who first held out to me a will-o'-the-wisp of hope that, though it may not be possible to throw advancing age into reverse, yet there might be a gleam of chemical promise of prolonging what was left of my prime of life. He intimated that the disintegration that scared me *might* be partly due to a hormone hunger.

Hormones? They were supposed to be the chemical messengers of the animal body. Hormones of innumerable kinds were supposed to be manufactured by various organs and glands in the body, to pass into the blood, and then to excite different and distant parts of the body to chemical activity.

I knew that insulin was one such hormone, manufactured by the pancreas, and thyroxin another typical hormone manufactured by the thyroid gland. Then too I had heard of the female hormones, estrone and estradiol, made by the ovaries. I knew that the testicles secreted testosterone (accent on the second syllable and rhyming with alone) but beyond this my knowledge of hormones was vague.

This was in the early nineteen-forties, and I listened skeptically to Herman Bundesen's mysterious hints about this new hormone science. I had a vague idea that his view of it wasn't exactly medically orthodox. The possibility of any restoration of man's waning energy by the male sex hormone particularly (and this was what Bundesen hinted) was certainly not generally admitted by the authorities on the new science of hormones who were discussing the subject in widely read medical journals. Moreover the idea sounded fishy because it was sexy—and who hadn't heard that monkey glands were the bunk? Yet, knowing Herman Bundesen as I was coming to do, I thought twice before selling him short on any medical project that he sponsored.

Among all medical and public health men that I knew, Bundesen was outstanding for his hatred of death, of all death, even that of the most lowly, and for his love of life, lusty life, long life, not only for himself but for all mankind, even the most humble. There is this peculiarity among men of medicine that has always puzzled me. The great majority of them (even including many of those who are technically most competent) are ashamed of being called death fighters. It seems as if they've been conditioned, by the medical profession's ten thousand years of mystical priesthood, into an emotion of respect for the inevitability of death—despite the life-giving power of the new weapons that their own science has placed in their hands. One eminent obstetrician said to me recently with pity and a trace of scorn of my lay enthusiasm and ignorance, "After all, we can't save *all* the mothers." This was the opposite of Herman Bundesen's spirit. He was privately laughed at for his fantastic assertion that there was no irreducible minimum in his fight to cut down the dying of mothers and their newborn babies.

There is a belittlement of their own glorious life-saving science to be found in the high priesthood of the medical profession. The millions of plain men and women (who are hellbent to live) come to their doctors bearing rave notices of the power of sulfas, penicillin, vitamins, and hormones, only to be met by a condescending, "Yes, but . . . these new remedies are abused; yes, but . . . they have their dangers; yes, but . . . they have their limitations, and they can't save all of you." Against these fainthearts, Herman Bundesen stood out as an optimistic strongheart who'd at least *try* new science on the gamble that it might give life to everybody.

He would always take a Brodie, and his intellectual humility was so deep that he was not ashamed to be wrong.

That's where Herman Bundesen differed from your typical medico-scientific big shots, so many of whom become and remain big shots by their reputations for never having been wrong about anything. They are sound men; and soundness demands refraining from the sticking out of the neck that is one characteristic of pioneers.

It is a gross error of narration that, in the above paragraphs, I've been speaking of Herman Bundesen in the past tense, as though he were already a ridiculous victim of his delusion that he was going to go on living and working forever. Today, almost ten years my senior, Herman has a head of thick blond hair, beginning to go gray; but his tanned skin is almost as smooth as that of a boy and with hardly a wrinkle. He is super-charged. He begins, optimistic and merry as a grig, at seven in the morning and leaves me in a definitely pooped condition at ten in the evening—himself to go home to work on his public health plans and writing. There is a fierce young gleam in his wise old gray eyes. Though always advocating the blessings of plenty of sleep, a balanced diet, a bottle of milk a day, and protection from drafts, he is the opposite of a self-coddling valetudinarian.

He plays ducks and drakes with what should be his diminishing store of energy at the age of sixty-two. I've seen him come to work in the morning, red-eyed from a nearly sleepless night of working, and watched his eyes clear and his face change from sallow to rosy as the new day's work thickens around him. His office is a kaleidoscopic bedlam of scientific, political, public health, and sometimes buffoonish activity.

He sits behind his enormous desk, the benevolent despot of Chicago's life and death; studying new plans for venereal disease eradication; interviewing (and outwitting) tough Chicago politicians; bawling out lazy health department nurses and then sending them out on their toes, lifted by a final kindly pep-talk; playing the prosecutor and putting the fear of God into the heart of the administrator of a dirty hospital where a mother has needlessly died in childbirth; talking long-distance for half an hour to some Washington bigwig trying respectfully to honey him out of a million dollars for a new hospital; taking time off to give a down-and-out doctor a job that may make a new man of him; talking fifteen minutes over the telephone to cajole a belligerent alderman; flying into a red-faced rage with his health officers because they've allowed a case of diphtheria to appear in Chicago; scanning death certificates of the city and fuming—not impotently—at the needless dying of a Negro baby; entertaining a famous English health administrator who suavely assures him that health officers in the eastern part of the United States, while they acknowledge Chicago's low death rate, do not like Bundesen's methods.

"I don't like my methods either," roars Herman Bundesen. "But, Godammit, they're the only ones I know that'll keep people from dying."

At the end of such a day—having had no time to eat anything—he refreshes himself with a couple of whiskey-sodas. "As we grow older," he says sagely, "our bodies become deficient in certain necessary alcohols." Then he tucks away a steak, relaxing only slightly; and after that, he is ready for an evening of planning a campaign to knock the gonococcus out of Chicago.

For more than twenty-two years Bundesen has been Chicago's health commissioner where it is as much as your official (and sometimes your physical) life is worth to fight for the health of the city's people amid that savage city's cynical and lusty contempt for life, and amid its notorious corruption. His own life's candle stays miraculously long though he has burned it, life-long, at both ends.

In his early forties, Bundesen ordered the extermination of four hundred thousand tuberculous cattle in the Chicago area, laughed at the threats of politicians and farmers to send him to jail, and wiped bone and gland tuberculosis out of Chicago's children.

In his middle forties, Bundesen defied Al Capone himself, closed down a notorious house of prostitution in a fight against syphilis, and for the first time in the country's history, put the word "syphilis" on the front pages of the newspapers.

In his late forties, in an interim from his health commissionership as Cook County's coroner, Bundesen, by using Goddard's ballistic crime-detecting science, gave the business (in one way or another) to all of the five St. Valentine's Day gangster murderers, put the fear of justice (illegal or otherwise) into the hearts of the hoodlums, and drastically cut down Chicago's homicide rate.

One day he looked into the mouth of a gat held close to his face. "When the guy pulled the trigger and the gun misfired, that was the last time I was scared," said Bundesen.

In his middle fifties he rallied the city's eminent, polite, and competent obstetricians for a knock-down-and-drag-out fight against ignorant and incompetent doctors who were killing mothers and babies in childbirth. He drove the Chicago death rate for newborn babies down to the lowest in the world.

Nearing sixty, Bundesen was indicted by the Federal Government for complicity in holding up the price of Chicago's milk. There were rumors that he was himself a bigtime grafter; and Bundesen—alone of all those accused—refused to take a consent decree offered by Thurman Arnold, defied the Department of Justice to try him, and without that trial was triumphantly vindicated in his fight to make Chicago's milk the safest in the U.S.A.

Now past sixty, he organized the Chicago Intensive Treatment Center against venereal disease. To break the chain of syphilitic infection, in the face of opposition and jeers by high medical authorities, he installed a mass test of the one-day, fever-chemical, and other intensive methods of treat-

ment of the disease. In the last half of 1943, Chicago had become venereally the safest of any large city in America for
the recreation of the boys of our armed forces.

When a man of such versatile public health accomplish-
ment and such seemingly inexhaustible energy tells you that
there *may* now be a scientific weapon to prolong life's prime,
you're inclined to listen.

CHAPTER THREE

IT WAS Herman Bundesen's hunch that sexual vigor is in some way tied up with the total vitality of animals and men. It was not original with him, being based on observations as old as mankind itself. It is not for nothing, for example, that the Spanish slang word for courage is *"cojones"*—testicles. But efforts to give old men new testicles had notably failed, and science had failed to prove its power to keep aging sex glands going. Now in the late nineteen-thirties, Bundesen learned that certain foreign chemists had actually trapped a pure male hormone, that they had discovered its precise chemical composition, and then synthesized what seemed to be the quintessence of the male sex glands. Bundesen dreamed of a bold new possible use of this chemical weapon.

For many years he had been a shrewd observer of the rise and fall of the great in Chicago. Long before this discovery of the pure male hormone, it had come to his notice that one of the most important business tycoons of the Midwest, then at the top of his financial magnificence, was sexually not at all the man he used to be. Bundesen held a modest block of stock in one of this man's enterprises, and banker friends assured the health commissioner that these shares were sure to increase tremendously in value. Bundesen shook his head owlishly, smiled with no explanation, and ordered that his own shares be disposed of at once. To himself he argued that, in the fierce competition of American business life, it's unwise to string along with business leaders after their male hormone has vanished. Not long after he had sold his stock, that business empire collapsed. "But how did you know it, Herman?" his friends asked him; and Bundesen replied only with that owlish smile.

Now a male hormone was captured, available. And now Bundesen planned a broad use of it, undreamed of by chemists, biologists, and physicians who were then cautiously testing its eerie powers on capons and eunuchoid and castrated men. He stated his hunch to me, by asking a question, by a comparison that was as original as it was simple and poetic.

"If chemicals can restore the yield of worn-out soil, can we not hope to renew the tissues and energy of worn-out men?" asked Bundesen.

This death fighter was the most curious combination of super-optimism and conservative scientific soundness that I had known. Now his bold projection of such a use for the new male hormone shocked me.

"Are you sure the male hormone is the chemical key to lost male vigor?" I asked him. "That worn-out tycoon of yours isn't enough to prove your point. He may be a misleading series of just one case," I taunted him.

"He's not the only case I know," said Bundesen.

"There must be plenty of old codgers," I offered, "who are has-beens in bed, but still've got brain power and fighting spirit."

"Who are they?" asked Bundesen.

I felt myself blushing. It is one of Bundesen's annoying and valuable traits never to accept generalities but always to insist upon evidence, even when his own generalities have a not very heavy backing. He would have made a devastating district attorney. Now I couldn't answer him, having conducted no poll for evidence of leading Americans keeping their top working and fighting stride despite loss of the old power of their *cojones*. . . . Was I myself the writer and fighter I used to be?

CHAPTER FOUR

WE ARE part of all we have met, and long before meeting Bundesen, I had been conditioned against hopes for science ever being able to extend life's prime by another medical worthy who, in his way, was a personality nearly as overwhelming as Chicago's health commissioner. This was my old professor of pathology at the University of Michigan Medical School, Doctor Aldred Scott Warthin. He was a short, plump, oval-shaped, not-very-tall man with a ruddy face and bright, merry eyes and a professional gray beard that would be the envy of any old-fashioned doctor. To us students, he was a terror. Before ever we entered medical school, and while we were still freshmen, pre-medic, he mowed us down with a lecture (illustrated by chancrous and ulcerous lantern slides) that warned us of the awful venereal fate awaiting us unless we remained celibate till we could marry some nice clean girl. Warthin was one of the greatest authorities on the pathology of syphilis the world had ever known; and his microscope had spotted the old ral in the bodies of defunct dignitaries in many walks of life. (His detractors hinted that Warthin saw syphilis spirochetes in his sleep, and sometimes, under his microscope, when they were not there.)

Yet, scaring us out of sexual peccadilloes in his brilliant and jolly way, Doctor Warthin was far from being an Anthony Comstock. Interspersed among his serious pathology lectures were sexy anecdotes that rocked his classes with laughter. He intimated himself to be a devotee of Eros, but strictly legitimately; and (like Bundesen) he thought that high-voiced, sissified men were unlikely to contribute importantly to mankind's progress. Yes, it was our duty to the perpetuation of the race to copulate, but always with benefit of clergy; and it was more than a duty, it was good clean fun. Then followed an intriguing dissertation on what the young married man and woman should know but too often, lamentably, didn't.

You may think this characterization of my great old teacher a bit frivolous and irrelevant, but it is really germane to our story, because Warthin, though he was appalled by the pathologic results of sexual sin and revelled in descriptions of marital happiness, was somberly certain that little or nothing would ever scientifically be done to extend man's all too short phase of sexual activity. Furthermore, and in contradiction to Bundesen, Doctor Warthin laughed at the notion that, by sexual rejuvenation, any worn-out man could return to his banking, business, engineering, fighting, or legal eminence.

The theme song of this brilliant and genial pathologist was that death is the inevitable consequence of life. Our merry professor was the most pessimistic pathologist in medical history. Through his microscope, his gimlet eye had peered at hundreds of thousands of gaily-painted, thin sections of the livers, hearts, brains, and kidneys of scores of thousands of luckless mortals who had fallen far short of reaching the Biblical three score years and ten. He had lived in the formaldehyde reek of the dead-house, his sharp knives had slashed into the corpses of hundreds of people who may have hoped to live to a hundred but had died before they were fifty. To Warthin, death was not only necessary, but it was beautiful because it wasn't you, the individual man, that mattered, because it was your principal use and destiny to live only long enough to procreate new life—for which there'd be no room on earth if you, the procreator, didn't pretty soon up and die.

Warthin was a rotund, florid, energetic, bouncing, and sometimes laughing, man whose philosophy was ghoulish. He was at the same time a martinet as a teacher; and most of his students had a fear of his path lab course, the hardest to pass in the entire four years of medical study. To our callow minds that made him super-impressive and ultra-credible.

In 1929, not very long before he died, Doctor Warthin published his swan song. It was a terrible and beautiful book entitled *Old Age*. Not only for himself, but for any man's hope to live a moment longer than God had planned, this book was a requiem. In powerful prose, seldom equaled by any medical writer, Warthin mocked at fears of age and death. It was this fear, he said, that prevented our talking scientifically and sensibly about growing old.

There was already then, at the end of the nineteen-twenties, a hope that the riddle of too early aging might at last be solved by exact knowledge of hormones. Warthin mocked the hormone hunters, telling them that for all their bright, but silly, experimental hopes, old age is utterly, invincibly (and happily) inevitable. By brilliant examples, he proved that, before we're born, parts of us start to die; that, as youth blooms into maturity, some of our tissues are already senile; that aging is the inexorable doom of all our body cells; that old age, in all of our cells, is irreversible.

Reading that book, I could see Warthin again as he was when he awed me as a student, overwhelmingly convincing with his immense dead-house learning. Now, in that book, his eloquence made me feel that my deep wish to live lustily to a very great age was really antisocial. "Inasmuch," he wrote, "as the reproductive function is the chief one of the individual life . . . it is but logical to conclude that when the carrier of the immortal germ plasm (meaning me) has arrived at maturity and continued at that stage long enough (again meaning me) to have secured its survival in his progeny, he, himself (finally meaning me), is then in the way of evolution." (The parentheses are mine.)

Warthin seemed to rejoice in death in those last years when he, himself, was getting ready to die. In his book *Old Age*, he quoted an old folk-saying, making it printable by paraphrasing the present participle of its four letter word. "When the reproductive capacity has ceased, then a man is as good as dead." Warthin said that this proverb was based upon an absolute foundation fact. Yet, there were examples contradicting him. Leeuwenhoek, first of the microbe hunters, had made some of his most marvelous observations when he was past seventy and far beyond connubial bliss; Pasteur had conquered the rabies terror long after he had any further hopes of fatherhood. And as for living things being in the way of evolution after they've secured the survival of their progeny, look at elephants, parrots, and certain turtles. They live to immense ages, surviving long after they've seen their babies off to a good start in life.

It was clear that Doctor Warthin was an extremely prejudiced man, on the side of death, just as Herman Bundesen (much less academically learned) was prejudiced on the side of life.

In their struggle for my allegiance, Warthin had this advantage. He had been my most feared professor, and, scaring me, his words conditioned me in favor of his gloomy slogan that death was the inevitable consequence of life.

CHAPTER FIVE

In those years of the nineteen-thirties when my virility was on the wane, Bundesen was following the unfolding chemical science of the sex hormones. In this he showed his usual courage, swimming upstream against a strong current of scientific respectability. Procreation, for all its biologic dignity, is a bit dirty. To look for the secret of total vitality in the testicles seems somewhat raffish to the more refined type of medical professor. The aspiration of an old man to be a postgraduate Romeo is more than a little disgusting to the majority of respectable people (including scientists) who do not share Bundesen's joy in all the functions of life.

In his witty way, Warthin made sport of the sex hormone hunters. He was very funny about these sexy experimenters. What about Voronoff, the ring-tailed monkey gland man? And what about that sensational Austrian, Steinach, who claimed he could restore the vitality of old rats and old men by tying off the ducts that led from their testicles? Of course, such science had two strikes on it before it went to the batter's box; there's something disreputable to your truly refined scientist about old man Winter on the make for Miss April. Warthin dismissed Voronoff's and Steinach's claims by hooting at them. If their operations had any effect at all, it was only a re-erotization, if any. He didn't feel it necessary to repeat their experiments. He simply issued a pathological excommunication against them.

"We may be assured," he wrote, "that there is no rejuvenescence possible for the senile individual; and the idea of physical rejuvenation is but a myth of ancient lineage disguised in quasi-scientific garments." In effect, he lumped all sex hormone hunters with foolish old Ponce de Leon looking in vain for his fountain of youth in the land of Bimini.

What a contrast, Warthin, the man of the dead-house, and Bundesen, the fighter for life. Warthin demolished any thought that death might ever be anything but early, invincible and inevitable, by well-chosen words. Bundesen clutched at every straw of hormone hope that might enable him and all other men to remain vigorous, if even only for a year, a month, even a day longer than fate intended. At the time of his death, Warthin did seem to have the best of the argument; and yet it would have been great fun to have taken these two, so-opposite doctors on a tour of laboratories where certain obscure and seemingly hare-brained chemical adventures were being launched at the beginning of the nineteen-thirties.

At the University of Chicago our two worthies, the one rejoicing in death and the other loving life, might now have watched Dr. Fred Koch and his students at their strange enterprise of extracting tons of the testicles of bulls with benzene, acetone, and other solvents—to trap a trace of chemical quintessence of unknown composition that performed the minor miracle of making a few capons conduct themselves (for a few days) like roosters.

Our jovially pessimistic Doctor Warthin would have pointed out that there weren't enough bulls in the world to revive the lustiness of more than a handful of old men for more than one evening. Bundesen, excited, would have answered, "Well, that would be *something!*"

Of course all science (so far as its human use goes) seems silly in its beginning, and that's what discourages searchers who are too practical and haven't a rich vein of fantasy. In those days, Bundesen and Warthin could have gone to Germany to observe the organic chemist, Butenandt. With Teutonic solemnity, that earnest man could have shown them a tiny tube. Sealed in it was a will-o'-the-wisp of actually crystalline sex hormone, chemically pure, of a definite melting point and molecular weight—androsterone. After long and laborious extractions and odoriferous chemical cookings, Butenandt had recovered this next-to-nothing out of twenty-five thousand liters of human urine!

So far as its promise for extending human vitality went, Warthin might justifiably have compared this research to a quest for perpetual motion. Bundesen, owlish, might have asked Butenandt to calculate how much hormone he could extract from the millions of gallons of urine daily going to waste down the world's drainpipes.

Then they could have visited the Zurich laboratory of the Jugoslav chemist, Ružička. He was busy, then, trying to transform the compound, cholesterol (common in the bodies of animals and men), into a sexual elixir. Warthin might have remarked that if nature had intended us to live in a perpetual springtime of vitality, she would have done the job herself, in our living bodies, where chemical synthesis is immensely more subtle and easy than it is in the laboratory. Bundesen, on the other hand, would have asked Ružička to send him a sample of the new male hormone the moment he'd accumulated enough of it to spare.

CHAPTER SIX

I CONFESS that I, myself (before I'd begun to examine seriously into this new hormone chemistry, about which Herman Bundesen hinted so mysteriously), was inclined to side with Warthin. Medically, in the early nineteen-thirties, this new breed of organic chemists had little prestige or influence. Medical science (aside from a certain amount of analysis of urine and blood) was a long way from being chemical. It was dominated by pathologists, like Warthin. Its heroes (aside from Pasteur and the microbe hunters, whose science chiefly saved babies and children) were physicians, like the great Sir William Osler. If Osler had still been alive, he would have thought Bundesen was crazy. Longer life, indeed! And by sex hormones! Osler was a doctor compared to Aesculapius and Hippocrates. Osler was the doctor's doctor. He was famous, not so much for the thousands of lives he had saved, as for his uncanny insight in diagnosing what it was that was going to kill a man, and then proving that his diagnosis was correct when he cut that man up in the dead-house. It was said of Osler that when he prepared to go from the wards to the autopsy room, it was then that he was like a white-plumed knight in shining armor. He was pretty much of a defeatist about curing any disease that was really serious; he was famous for his wonderful sympathy at the bedside that made it not quite so terrible for people to die.

Osler and Warthin, together, would certainly have made hash of Bundesen's hopes. In one of the most memorable of all Osler's speeches, he said (only partly in fun?) that men did their real work before they were forty and should be chloroformed at sixty. This mood of resignation against death was stamped, by Osler, upon modern medicine. So, in searching for a straw of hope against on-coming old age (not yet having looked into Herman Bundesen's hints about a new and powerful hormone) I found little to encourage me.

It is true that there was now a new division of medical practice, called geriatrics. It was the opposite of pediatrics and dealt with the medical care of the old. In it I delved, but with terrible disappointment, for advice on how to keep myself fighting, vigorous, and young, like Bundesen. Geriatrics was a careful science. Its exponents told me that, to preserve my kidneys, I should keep out of Lake Michigan's cold water in the Spring and Autumn; it advised me to keep out of drafts because pneumonia was the enemy of aging men; it warned me to stop dune-climbing and too much cross-cut sawing because these would put a strain on my heart muscle; it told me that another inch round my middle was another year off my life and that I should concern myself a great deal with the care of my bowels; I should not bound out of bed saying, "Oh, what a beautiful morning," but, instead, should take breakfast in bed, if possible, and get up and dress with the careful deliberation of old Mr. Rockefeller, Sr., trying to nurse himself along to live to a hundred; it admonished me to keep out of battles that would worry me: apoplexy, coronary occlusion, diabetes, and maybe cancer, might result from worry unavoidable in a life of fierce competition.

In short, geriatrics was a sissy science, a horrible compendium of what an old man should know. It was no fight against old age. It was its appeasement. Old age was not chemical, not for geriatricians. Old age was something geriatricians probably wanted people to arrive at so that they could practice their unimaginative palliations—the sad opposite of the lustiness that pediatricians can give to children. For pediatricians, old age was a tragi-comic poem of the inevitable, and Warthin was its Homer. One of the very best consulting physicians I've ever known—Dr. L. G. Christian of Lansing, Michigan, not primarily a geriatrician—actually gave Warthin's book, *Old Age*, as a prescription to middle-aged men who came to him complaining they were not what they used to be. And, mind you, Greg Christian was the kind of doctor that wanted people to *live*. Yet he told his slipping patients just to read that book, to take their old age and like it.

I had the deepest respect for Greg's medical wisdom; yet, arbitrarily, I resented this medical resignation; I wanted to go on swimming, working, and fighting. Arguing with my pessimistic medical friends, I brought up a series of one case. Look at Herman Bundesen, so notably defying his dissolution.

"Yes, maybe," said one doctor, smiling, "but watch Bundesen. One of these days he'll blow up like a cannon."

CHAPTER SEVEN

I TURNED, at last, to remembering the fundamental science of Jacques Loeb. I had known and worshipped this most brilliant of modern biologists many years before. I knew that his remote, cold, theoretical, icily optimistic experiments could be of no practical help to me as of now. But their fundamental promise might help my morale while I waited to see whether Bundesen's hints about the coming of a new vital chemical were more than mere wishful thinking. Though Jacques Loeb was an M.D., he hooted at the bedside wisdom of physicians, and made sport of pessimistic pathologists.

He was really the forerunner of those organic chemists, hormone hunters like Fred Koch toiling with bull testicles in Chicago, Butenandt extracting oceans of urine in Göttingen, Ružička dabbling dangerously with cholesterol in Zurich—in all of whom Bundesen professed faith. Jacques Loeb was a chemical John the Baptist who was not properly a chemist at all. He was an optimistic Moses among experimental biologists, destined not to reach the Promised Land his own science predicted.

Loeb's fierce belief in the power of experimental science did give me courage to doubt Warthin's ghoulish wisdom, even though Loeb promised nothing at all for my own future. You could at least say this about Loeb's experiments, devoted though they were to such miserably sub-human creatures as sea urchins and starfish: they threw grave doubts upon Warthin's wisecrack that death is the inevitable consequence of life. Loeb was a very witty atheistical man whose religion it was that all living things are nothing but machines and that all life—lowest to highest—is simply physico-chemical, and fixable.

In Jacques Loeb's theology, life was the purely accidental consequence of the interplay of blind forces. God? He might be only the chemical molecule. The Son? He might be the atom. The Holy Spirit? It might be the energy that drew chemical compounds together or tore them apart. No, that's making Loeb a bit more blasphemous than he really was. Loeb had a fierce faith in the power of man, in human ingenuity, in human dignity. Man himself was God. The day would come when man, taking thought, would change the heretofore inexorable chemistry that made men hate each other, destroy each other, and that sent men prematurely to their graves. For all his materialism, Jacques Loeb was a deeply religious man, believing that ultimate human brotherhood would be brought about by physics and chemistry. Maybe men would arise who would change today's fatal chemistry of too early death in my favor, in my time? Loeb, the far opposite of a charlatan, didn't promise that. It was enough that he predicted that some day it might come true.

Warthin was literary, Bundesen was a man of action, but Loeb was an experimenting Prometheus. Loeb had the overpowering personality of your highest type of European man of culture and brains, in the tradition of Darwin, Pasteur, and Gregor Mendel. He was lean and not tall, Jewish, hatchet-faced, clean-cut, handsome, with very bright eyes that held me, fascinated me as he discoursed on what chemistry might do to transform the fate of sea urchins and men.

Opened wide, Loeb's eyes seemed to look through you and six feet into the ground back of you; and again they'd gleam roguishly through narrow slits that were flanked by webs of wrinkles as he laughed at gutless pathologists and medicos who couldn't stomach his own cold mechanistic conception of life.

In the scientifically somber and mentally proper atmosphere of the Rockefeller Institute as it was in those days of the nineteen-twenties, Loeb was an impish throwback to a more optimistic age of mankind; he was a twentieth century scientific Voltaire. His devastating wit was feared at the Institute's lunch table where it was not manners to get funny with big shots in any walk of life. Loeb indiscriminately demolished bishops who disbelieved in the theory of Evolution; denounced evolutionists who thought life's development was inevitable and not to be changed by the mighty new weapon of chemistry. He was a militant pacifist and was bitter against chauvinists (among whom he ridiculed Teddy Roosevelt especially) because their wars led to mass human death. He blistered pathologists with a gay scorn because they still dominated medicine with their learned folderol that was merely a description of what they saw, peering through their microscopes at thin slices of mice and men who were dead.

"Pathology!" Loeb would exclaim. "My boy, dat iss not *science!*"

Loeb was all for life, and with an intensity that made you sometimes think he'd invented it himself. He was creative. He was a dabbler—however crude—in the dark and secret caverns of primitive life, and here he had a genius for stating the most complex problems with childlike simplicity, and he was a wizard at simple experimentation. With a few clean watch glasses, flasks and pipettes, with sea-water and a few simple chemicals, he made mighty inquiries into the machinery of life's beginning. His simple chemical potterings ripped away the superstitious sexy mystery that beclouded the manner in which living creatures began to live, to develop the moment after the sperm of the male penetrated the egg of the mother.

Here before his slit eyes in a watch glass lay the eggs of a miserable marine animal, the sea urchin. God had never meant those eggs to develop, to live, without the sperm of the male. From these unfertilized eggs Jacques Loeb now produced actual swimming larvae, miraculously fatherless by an experiment where chemicals pinch-hit for the spermatozoon.

His childish magic caused the unfertilized eggs to begin to divide, to grow, to become swimming creatures by a treatment with sea-water, the chemistry of which he only slightly altered by adding a small but definite quantity of salt or sugar. When he put those eggs back into normal sea-water, they developed, a part of them forming an intestine and even a skeleton absolutely without benefit of the sperm of the father.

He demolished the age-old superstition that youngsters are necessarily the fruit of marriage. His experiments were a crude, yet breath-taking promise that the mysteries of sex are chemical. His results got onto the front pages of newspapers, nationwide, where it was erroneously alleged that this German Jewish genius had created life itself.

Yet this was a fact, that he had imitated the primordial, life-starting action of the sperm, by chemistry.

Loeb, for me, was mentally like a ripping northwest Lake Michigan gale blowing away Warthin's decadent verbalism that reeked of life's defeat, always wailing that death is the inevitable consequence of life. Loeb laughed at the defeatist word, inevitable. Whatever fate had decreed inevitable, man could change. For him one simple experiment was worth all the metaphysical millions of words of the philosophers that had presumed to explain life and had only beclouded it. Was life the entrance of some mysterious, intangible life principle into the egg? Did death come to our bodies with that life principle's departure?

Loeb hooted at such a play on words. Life principle, indeed! "Scientifically, individual life begins," said Loeb, "with the acceleration of the rate of oxidation in the egg." He proved it in the case of the sea urchin. He had a fiery faith that it was true for men.

Death was no more mysterious. "Life in warm-blooded animals—man included—ends with the cessation of oxidation in the body," said Loeb. "The problem of the beginning and the end of individual life is physico-chemically clear."

For this bold and primitive engineer of living machinery all that happened, from the cradle to the grave, was a consequence of oxidation. The wishes and hopes, efforts and struggles, and unfortunately also the disappointments and sufferings, shouldn't all this be amenable to physico-chemical analysis? He was the strange twin intellectual brother of Charles F. Kettering, today's torchbearer of that most difficult and cold crusade, the battle-cry of which is that life's tragedy will finally be conquered by science. "In spite of the gulf which separates us today from such an aim (to explain all life physico-chemically) I believe that it is attainable," said Loeb.

Undaunted by the shifting mystery of life, Loeb, like Kettering, knew that all problems, when solved, turn out to be simple. "As long as a life phenomenon has not yet found a physico-chemical explanation it usually appears inexplicable," said Loeb. Then heigh-ho for new experiments with seawater, pipettes, little animals, and chemicals. "When the veil is once lifted, we are always surprised that we did not guess from the first what was behind it."

By adding a small but definite amount of acid to water in which little creatures were swimming, who were indifferent to light, he changed them into beings who swam, willy-nilly, toward a flame. He predicted sex hormones and their terrific power over the actions of living beings. The nuptial flight of ants and bees was really nothing mysterious or romantic. It was only another example of that attraction to light that's called heliotropism. It was only the chemical result of sexual maturity.

On the maybe flimsy platform of these experiments Jacques Loeb made the boldest prophecies.

"If we can call forth in an animal otherwise indifferent to light, by means of an acid, a heliotropism that drives it irresistibly to the flame; if the same thing can be brought about by means of a secretion of the reproductive glands (today we'd say hormone) we have given, I believe, a group of facts, within which the analogies necessary for psychiatry can be called forth experimentally and can be investigated."

Did that mean that lack of sex hormones, or too much of them, might actually drive men crazy?

Jacques Loeb was immensely ahead of his time and yet so brilliant is the blitz war of science against the unknown, that here in the late nineteen-thirties was Bundesen hinting to me that such miracles were already being made by hormone-hunting biologists and physicians. Loeb was the man I should tie to, and to hell with the geriatricians and lovers of death.

Against the inevitability of death again Loeb was a forerunner. His own brother, Leo Loeb, had begun a strange new science by which, technically, you could remove a bit of tissue from an animal or a man, and set it to growing in a nutrient soup under sterile precautions as you grow microbes. Leo Loeb's followers had found this amazing fact: by proper methods of tissue cultivation, carefully lifting those bits of living tissue from old soup into new, they did not grow old, they did not die, they went on living, far beyond the term of life of the animals or human beings they came from, they would live as long as there were human beings to transplant them from tube or glass dish to the next one!

"This points to the idea," said Jacques Loeb, "that death is not inherent in the individual cell. Death is only the fate of the more complicated organisms in which different types of cells and tissues are dependent upon each other."

Wouldn't some future pipette wizard, simple and bold like Loeb, discover the chemical and physical secret of the battle of life against death that raged in my own aging body, I pondered.

"In this case," Loeb went on (the case of death of more complicated organisms), "it seems to happen that one or certain types of cells and tissues produce a substance which gradually becomes harmful to a vital organ."

Wouldn't Bundesen's new heroes, these organic chemists, spot that murderous chemical? I wondered.

"The mischief of death," Loeb finished it, "may then be traced to the activity of a black sheep in the society of tissues and organs."

And yet, and yet remembering another side of Loeb, I had the right to be gloomy. He had little or no respect for the chemical dabblers with human life in the Rockefeller Institute Hospital and the great university medical schools. "You see," he'd say, with a contemptuous chuckle, while a warm smile made crowsfeet round his glittering eyes, "dat iss not science."

Then he'd take the bite out of his jeering at his bungling medical colleagues by a completely detached demolition of his own scientific life. "You understand," he'd say, "I haf made de most foolish possible mistake. I haf liffed my own life backvardts. I began by trying to do exact vork on sharks and dogs. Dey ver too complicated. Now here I am at de endt of my life. I haf kept vorking all de time with littler and littler animals. I thought dey vouldt be simpler and simpler. Now here I vork only with proteins, colloids. And I findt *dey* are yet too complicated!"

So it was still remote, this defeat of old age and death. Yet Loeb's faith in the omnipotence of experiment kept stoking up my own wishful thinking and hoping that some small chemical miracle might somewhat delay my arrival at the state of the slippered pantaloon.

CHAPTER EIGHT

WASN'T Jacques Loeb a bit too pessimistic about the death fight of the immediate future? He was not long cold in his grave in the middle nineteen-twenties when the science of life or death began to turn a corner. A new breed of death fighters was rising. It was a teamwork of chemists, physicists and engineers who began joining forces with a few medical men who were bold like Bundesen. It was not that these men were exceptionally able doctors; it was that they were not gently resigned to death, like Osler; it was that they were not jubilantly cocksure about the inevitability of early dying, like Warthin; it was that they had a blind faith that chemists and physicists could right now begin to forge weapons for their death-fighting arsenal.

These physicians and technical men defied the dead hand of the immense prestige of Sir William Osler. They had the guts to begin launching drives against diseases that Osler was sadly certain would always remain (quoting famous old English Doctor Sydenham) "continuate and inexorable."

The technical men knew nothing at all about disease or death; their new medical comrades were uncouth, irregular, heretical against the tradition of Osler because they believed nothing is impossible—till you've tried it. To Toronto, for example, from the empty reception room of his unsuccessful practice in London, Ontario, came an obsessed young Canadian surgeon, Frederick G. Banting. He had a crackpot plan for experiment that might lead to the control of diabetes, about which he was less than no authority at all. The then only hope for grown-ups, threatened with diabetic coma, was a starvation diet to which death itself seemed preferable; and as for diabetic children, there was no hope they'd ever live to man or womanhood.

Banting's proposal for certain dog experiments bored the University of Toronto's distinguished professor of pathology, J. J. R. Macleod. Banting had only this equipment: a stubborn temper. Gravely wounded in World War I, army surgeons said they must amputate Banting's arm or he would die. Damn them, then he'd die. He kept his arm for those experiments that his obstinacy finally caused Professor Macleod to let him perform, experiments resulting in the discovery of that hormone from the pancreas known as insulin. It was a crude brew almost as dangerous as it was powerful against fatal diabetes.

Then the organic and physical chemists set out to refine it; and today a child of eight or an old lady near eighty (as for example my own mother) can control their own diabetes, keep themselves living and strong by these little injections that are all that stand between themselves and death.

A fantastic obsession, unorthodox and crackpot, that was what insulin was—in the beginning.

There were diseases far more fatal than diabetes, for example, one hundred per cent deadly pernicious anemia. In Boston, Massachusetts, there lived a lean, tall and stubborn physician, George R. Minot. His own life had just been saved from severe diabetes by Banting's insulin. On the sly—so that his learned Harvard medical friends wouldn't laugh at him—Minot began feeding a small troop of pernicious anemia victims diets that were scientifically silly. With desperate enthusiasm, Minot kidded daily large meals of liver into these thin-blooded wretches who were (according to Osler) sure to die.

· They lived. They grew strong. Yet it couldn't last. Surely they'd soon gag at their necessarily enormous daily meals of liver that were all that stood between them and death. It was not practical. It was cruel to give them this short hope. Then came chemist Edwin Cohn, cooking and extracting and stewing and filtering this life-saving X in liver down to an approximate purity, high concentration and safety so that a dozen injections or so a year could keep these ex-doomed pernicious anemia people thick-blooded, strong and working.

There were diseases not killing worth-while civilized people but only Oriental have-nots, but killing them as dead as if they really were humanly important. In the Philippine Islands a young organic chemist, Robert R. Williams, crouched on the floor of a native hut. In the arms of its mother, a baby, blue-faced and gasping, was within minutes of death from beriberi. The child did not rate a doctor. Into the baby's mouth, Williams, chemist, experimenting, let fall a few drops of an extract of rice polishings.

Within a half hour healthy color returned to the baby, and its breathing grew even and strong, and it began crying and lived to laugh and play. This chemical miracle haunted Bob Williams into thirty years of chemical dreaming and cookery to find the way at last, in the middle nineteen-thirties, to synthesize the pure chemical that had actually saved that baby's life; it was the master vitamin, B_1, thiamin.

Getting thiamin pure, Williams did more than discover a simple chemical cure for beriberi. Jacques Loeb had said that life is basically oxidation. Thiamin now turned out to be one of the key chemicals that controlled what had seemed to be the hopelessly obscure and infinitely complicated machinery of oxidation in the bodies of all living beings.

Wasn't Jacques Loeb's hope for a chemical explanation of life coming faster than he'd dare to dream? Wandering out from a reeking old red brick laboratory building in Washington, D. C., Joseph Goldberger, a dreamy Jew, made medically laughed-at experiments. His animals? They were a red-rashed, weary, no-account, sometimes demented, rag-tag-and-bobtail of southern mankind, pellagrous. Dr. Goldberger's notions were hooted down by medical authority. He worked, entranced and oblivious. To lay his own gnawing doubts of his theory, he submitted himself to revolting self-experiment. He injected himself with the blood and ate the intestinal discharges of dying pellagrins.

He proved that pellagra was not infectious, by himself surviving, and discovered that this disease was really a hidden hunger. Twenty years later (alert to a happy accident) chemist Conrad Elvehjem of Wisconsin University tracked this dietary lack down to a simple organic chemical, nicotinic acid.

And now in the late nineteen-thirties certain desperately sick pellagrins were brought into Hillman Hospital in Birmingham, Alabama, on stretchers; they were stuporous, demented. On himself, Doctor Tom Douglas Spies had tested whether nicotinic acid (cousin of the powerful poison, nicotine) was safe for men. He survived huge doses. Then he gave those fantastic doses to these patients who before would have had not more than a fifty-fifty chance of coming out of that hospital alive.

These people arose and walked home the very same day they'd been brought in, demented and dying. And like thiamin, this simple organic chemical, nicotinic acid, was found to be another cog in the machinery of those cellular oxidations that Jacques Loeb said were the basic difference between life and death.

These events of the nineteen-twenties and nineteen-thirties could be called miracles in cold scientific print. Once the organic chemists had got them absolutely pure, or even sufficiently concentrated, they unlocked doors that, from time's beginning, had been slammed shut by death. If insulin, if liver extract, if pure vitamins, could make these miracles, then maybe Bundesen might be right when he hinted at the pure male hormone's power to revive and prolong the total vitality of men.

CHAPTER NINE

I<small>T WAS</small> plain that the science of life or death was now passing out of the hands of doctors resigned at the bedsides of the dying, that the new science was bubbling in the flasks and stills of the organic chemists. These were a new breed of men, thinking, talking, and working in a new human language, highly esoteric and expressed in the hieroglyphics of structural organic chemistry. I understood this new language a little. But I still smiled at Bundesen's faith in it. How many medical men would have the nerve to use the new male hormone to test out the proposition that a man is as old as his testicles?

The prevailing medical and scientific organization would be unlikely to go all out for such an undignified notion. The entire new assault upon inexorable death continued to lack respectability. The experimenting physicians, like stubborn Banting, illogical Minot, dreamy Goldberger, were only guerilla fighters in this new war against inexorable death. In this war the general staff of the regular army (the big professors and bosses of organized medicine) were defeatists. That is, till after the guerillas had proved their victories over and over. Even so, the number of lives so far saved was negligible.

What had the new teams of organic chemists and guerilla doctors accomplished against the degenerative diseases of the blood vessels, the real mass killers of human life in its prime? Next to nothing. Yet it was clear that growing old, for the immense majority, isn't natural, is a sickness. Here was the

36

scandal: the average life expectancy of a man was sixty-three, yet there were men who lived hale and hearty to eighty and even ninety. There was the famous instance of Sir William Mulock, the grand old man of Ontario, living to more than a hundred, though (so it was reliably reported) it was only in his last years that he had cut his Scotch whiskey drinking down to one bottle a day. Surely such miraculous old men as Mulock held a chemical secret (aside from the alcohol) in their bodies. Why wasn't there an immense medico-chemical research probing for it?

There was no serious, long-range, heavily-financed research into the riddle of too early aging. It was no use to discuss such a campaign with the deans of medical schools; their budgets for any kind of research were feeble and they were hard-pressed to keep the teaching part of their institutions going. By the time their young researchers had got to be professors, respectabilized, they no longer believed in scientific victory over the old age riddle.

Just the same, I kept looking and looking and at last found a gleam of encouragement that such a fight might be possible. I got to know Doctor Theodore G. Klumpp who was in his special way a guerilla. He was the far opposite of a professor and had a crazy optimism.

One evening, walking down Fifth Avenue in New York City in the bracing October weather, Ted Klumpp was enthusiastic about what the chemists might do for our arteries, if we could just hang on for a few years more. Ted belonged to a new breed of men in medicine. Mentally he was keen as mustard. Before getting his medical degree at Harvard, he had observed the curative effect of liver upon the sore-mouthed and sometimes fatal sickness called sprue. Teaching at Yale University Medical School, he had shown brilliant promise as an internist. He had not stayed there long because he was restless against near-starvation for too many years.

Ted Klumpp was something of a rolling stone. He had

wandered from Yale to the Federal Food and Drug Administration to police purveyors of false cures. Then, for a very
short time, he had served as secretary to the Council on
Pharmacy and Chemistry of the American Medical Association, an excellent body of men who try earnestly to tell true
cures from false but with scant facilities to test them. Despite
the highly scientific resignation against death that Klumpp
had experienced at Yale, despite the quackish claims against
death he'd had to deal with in his jobs with the government
and the medical association, he retained a hatred against too
early old age and had an obsession that its chemical conquest
might be around some not too far-off corner.

So here he was at last, just turned forty and the president
of a great chemical company that made pharmaceuticals.
Klumpp was outwardly very conservative, a German-Ameri-
can, slow-spoken, lean, handsome in a rugged manner. As a
manufacturer responsible for stockholders' dollars, he could
not be a visionary. Now walking down Fifth Avenue, Ted
really surprised me.

"How'd you like to live, healthy, to, let's say, one hundred
and thirty?" he asked.

"Don't be an extravagant ass," I said, on guard because
my own writings were always being criticized for their
expansiveness.

"Biologically, most animal species live to about six times
the age it takes them to mature. We mature fully in the early
twenties. We *should* live to between one hundred and twenty
and thirty," said Ted.

"Fine—if the human species isn't the exception. Our arteries
go to hell long before that," I said gloomily.

"When I was examining patients at Yale," Klumpp answered, "here's what hit me. Some were senile at forty. Their
arteries were as hard and calcified as the stem of a clay pipe."

"Yes, and you couldn't reverse it," I said.

"Then there were others twice the age of those senile forty-year-olds. They had a twinkle in their eyes. Their arteries and their minds were elastic, past eighty."

"Of course, like old Sir William Mulock," I answered. "But such grand old men *inherit* their nice soft arteries."

"I didn't know you were such a scientific reactionary," said Klumpp.

"Remember Raymond Pearl's gag," I offered. "A careful selection of one's parents in respect of longevity is the most reliable form of personal life insurance."

"It doesn't mean a damn thing," said Ted. "Let's be chemical. It simply means that people in a long-lived line inherit a pattern of chemical behavior." That made me remember Jacques Loeb who'd said that the mischief of death must be traced to the activity of a black sheep in the society of our tissues and organs.

"You see," said Klumpp, "it's our blood circulation, it's the arteries that are the unit that's the least common denominator of longevity."

"So you think that's news," I kidded him. "A man is as old as his arteries. For God's sake, what a discovery!"

Klumpp was a German and stubborn and plodding. "How do our blood vessels age? They lose their elastic fibers and then scar tissue and calcium salts are deposited in their place. That's all there is to arteriosclerosis. That's what's behind degenerative disease," he generalized.

"Yes, that's all there's to it, and we don't know a damn thing about it, so let's stop kidding ourselves. You and your one hundred and thirty! Let's eat, drink, and be merry." I tried to bring Ted Klumpp down out of his vision.

It was no use. That night, till very late, in his slow-spoken stubborn way he kept chewing at the possibility of an old age fight while we sat at Jack and Charlie's "Twenty-One" in that mystic upstairs back room that has the water buffalo's head over the bar leering at you and seeming to know that here, though the deepest questions of life or death are discussed, they will never be settled. Like a sophomore medical student, Ted Klumpp kept making wild stabs for leads for chemical research into premature aging. The state of high illumination brought on by Barbados daiquiris, burgundy, brandy, and then whiskey, had the opposite mental effect on us.

"Drinking," expostulated Ted, "doesn't kill you and may even help to keep you alive if you'll only oxidize it. It only kills you when you start drinking yourself to death; and then when you feel that coming on, you can always join Alcoholics Anonymous."

We ate very large Brizzola steaks. What diets predispose to long living? Brizzola steaks are full of B vitamins. "The average length of life of the white rat," Ted pronounced, "has been extended ten per cent by high vitamin diets—and the rat is closest to us of all mammals, nutritionally speaking."

I brought up the examples of George Bernard Shaw and Doctor John Harvey Kellogg, immensely old, yet vegetarians.

We smoked long Amatista cigars, too many. Hadn't the late Raymond Pearl proved that smoking had an adverse effect upon longevity, I asked. "Pearl only proved that smokers are the kind of people, maybe hyper-energetic and nervous, who don't live long anyway," said Ted.

Ted looked at me critically. "Aren't you too fat to expect to live much longer," he asked. Ted is very lean and looks like Joel McCrea, while I am said to resemble an older edition of John L. Sullivan.

I answered that, of my three honorary uncles who remained vigorous into their eighties, Chase Osborn and Jack Miner were pretty bulky, and only old George Hebden Corsan was lean. Yet we mustn't forget that all three of them were teetotalers, non-smokers and lived in the fresh air and sunshine.

So we kept getting nowhere very fast, yet Ted kept grabbing for straws of hope. He brought up strange news of new science from the Soviet Union. "The Russian biologist,

Bogomolets," said Ted, "has reported a remarkable observation, made near Sukhum in the Caucasus."

Ted went on to say gravely that Bogomolets' workers in a few days had uncovered twelve old codgers from one hundred and seven to one hundred and thirty years old in one village, husky old duffers. Some were said to have climbed up into trees like young monkeys to pick fruit for the visiting scientists, and one was trying to make himself out only seventy (though he was really over a hundred) because he wanted to take himself a new bride.

I reflected on the many wars and revolutions that must have destroyed Russian records. "Did Bogomolets have reliable birth certificates on those old guys?" I asked, skeptically.

Ted countered that this Russian scientist, Bogomolets, believed he was getting at the chemical secret of aging. It lay in the connective tissue of our bodies. He'd actually got a serum against old age changes. It was called A C S—antireticular cytotoxic. "When the war's over," said Ted, "let's go to Russia to look into it."

"But those old guys in the Caucasus, jumping around in fruit trees, didn't live that long because of A C S," I protested. "Bogomolets didn't begin trying his A C S on humans till 1936."

Ted admitted there was no scientific confirmation of this magic A C S outside Russia. "Yes, and this A C S is too altogether damned wonderful," I said. "It is alleged not only to be good against aging. It's claimed to be effective against scarlet fever and cancer, dementia praecox and fractures."

So I talked like any orthodox medical professor while Ted protested it wasn't science to condemn any alleged discovery until other scientific men had tested it and failed to confirm it. Anyway weren't those Russians wonderful? Look at the way they'd torn the guts out of the Nazis, the best-equipped army in the world. "They're full of genius," said Ted. "They believe anything's possible. Look at Pavlov, look at Mendelejev."

Every time I tried to puncture Klumpp's optimism, he kept coming back to his organic chemists. "Let's hang on a few years," he said. "Just give those organic chemists a whack at what's back of the degeneration of our arteries."

Here he really had me. Ted Klumpp was one of the men who meant a new force in medicine, men who were the far opposite of resigned and defeatists, who were encouraging, stimulating and goading on the organic chemists, the formerly medically ignored industrial organic chemists. I remembered that it was in no highbrow medical school, but in the German I. G. Farben, that the terrific life-saving power of the sulfas had been discovered. It was in our own American chemical industry (American Cyanamid) that sulfadiazine, king of all the sulfas, had been developed. It was in Ted's own company (Winthrop Chemical) that the industrial chemist, Sherndal, had discovered the German secret of how to make the malaria-fighting drug, atabrine, which had done so much toward our winning the war in the Pacific. And which, together with mosquito control, could now begin to wipe malaria, mankind's chief killer, out of the civilized world. Even if the medical men still had to start most of the discoveries, the industrial organic chemists would finish them.

That night Ted Klumpp brought me back around to the hope hinted by Herman Bundesen, to a dream of the coming power of chemically pure hormones. Cancer was one of the master-killers lying in wait for us in our middle years. "Look at the new hormonal control of cancer of the prostate," said Ted.

I had to admit a gleam of hope here against at least one of the arch enemies of old age. Di-ethyl-stilbestrol, with its hormone-like action, was showing chemical control over cancer of the prostate that before could only be checked by castration. And now, ethinyl estradiol was proving itself fifteen times stronger. It was killing the pain, checking the spread of prostate cancer and putting victims back on their feet and working; and who knew, it might cure some of them.

"Why shouldn't our chemists find specific hormones to control the wild growth of every kind of cancer cell?" asked Klumpp, his eyes gleaming. "All the cells of our bodies are under the influence of one or more hormones," he said.

"And even hormones against too early old age?" I asked him.

"Why not?" he answered. "What have we done; how long are we going to wait to get started against this tragic riddle? You could buy all the research that's ever been done against old age for a few miserable million dollars. Compare our medical schools with their short-term researches and their stingy budgets to the scientific projects of the big motor companies, to your own friend, Boss Kettering, who spends millions of dollars researching into motor cars, Diesel engines, and fuels, not for next year but for fifteen years into the future. Compared to Kettering, our medical researchers are like soldiers attacking concrete forts with pop-guns. Our industrial researchers can already promise us a fabulous postwar world. But what the hell's the good of all their gadgets if *we* can't live long enough and strong enough to enjoy them?"

That night I left Ted Klumpp who was in the clouds with his dream of applying the power of the industrial organic chemists to the scandal of too early old age that the medical professors had so far so tragically fumbled. That night I determined to examine, with all the Dutch industry of which I was still capable, into hormone science that Herman Bundesen hinted was already in action in favor of a stronger and maybe a longer prime of life.

What were really the facts about this synthetic male hormone? I had heard it claimed that it could help worn-out animal and human bodies to rebuild themselves, at least partially; that it stimulated the synthesis of new proteins in the body; that it increased the size and power of muscles; that it enlarged and strengthened the secreting power of the cells of the kidneys; that it might actually give certain broken men a new lease on life. In the interests of propriety, it was unfortunate that this male hormone, in nature, was principally manufactured in the testicles. But in science there is nothing proper or improper. Mightn't this be a lead, not in any way the final answer, but maybe the first hint of a clue for the organic chemists Ted Klumpp said were going to lick the disease of old age? What about this male hormone with that curious lilting name—testosterone?

PART II

THE HORMONE HUNTERS

CHAPTER TEN

In the face of the heretofore absolute inevitability of the waning of the vigor of men, the organic chemists now trying to restore that vigor might seem to you to be incredibly fool-hardy and impudent. They might seem to be idiotic alchem-ists trying to turn lead into gold. Yet, now when I began digging down into the hieroglyphic records of what their super-modern cookery was actually doing, their lunatic en-terprise became more and more sensible. Their project to trap the secrets of total vitality seemed more and more sane as I began truly to understand the significance of the promise of their experiments to change life fundamentally. What they were doing was as new, as bold, as original as man's first taming of fire and required immensely greater mental effort; it was a milestone marking man's progress from apedom. This now became plain to me: till you understand structural organic chemistry as it dominates life, you can't comprehend today's science of life at all. This gave me cour-age against Osler and Warthin and those medical bigwigs of today who pooh-pooh the idea of man's adding a bit to life's prime. Why take these so-called authorities seriously? For-get about them. They are like those gibbering Neanderthal men who stood shaking their heads and shivering while they watched the new men warm themselves at dangerous fires in front of their caves. They didn't know organic chemistry. Then how could they sell it short? The vast majority of these medical reactionaries, if you stood them an examination in the rudiments of organic chemistry, couldn't draw you a

47

simple diagram showing the structural difference between an open chain and a ring carbon compound.

As I pored over the records of curious cookings, extractions, and distillations, it was clear that the organic chemists were not so crackpot in their enterprise of trying to rip the veil from the age-old mystery of the virility of men. With the new technical weapon of their organic chemistry they were only exploring a very ancient and crude, yet fundamental, human science that had been accumulating for thousands of years. From the beginning of human record, priests, saints, medicine men, farmers, and sultans had been demonstrating how clear-cut, sure, and simple it was to take the vigor of animals and men away.

How? By removing their testicles.

What they lacked was any power to restore that virility, once it was gone. Those myriads of holy men, sultans, and farmers (unconscious scientists) knew the negative of male hormone science. Why hadn't they tried the positive? They had proved millions of times over that castration took vigor away. Why hadn't they tried to put it back? While for their own purposes they tamed eunuchs, draft horses, and steers by taking away their sex glands, they, themselves, all aspired to stay as lusty as they could as long as possible. They knew that castration made young men old, suddenly. Why didn't they put two and two together?

Why didn't they reason that older men, losing their youth gradually, might also be suffering a slow, chemical castration taking place invisibly with the passage of time?

The answer's to be found, maybe, in the feebleness of the best human brain, in the gag for which Boss Kettering is famous, that nothing is so obscure as the obvious.

Of course it is true (according to Doctor Gerhard J. Newerla, who has written a brilliantly instructive story of the three thousand years it took to discover the male hormone) that certain ancients actually did try to restore human male vigor. Doctor Newerla writes that old Doctor Susruta of India in 1400 B.C. recommended that Hindus eat testicles as a cure for their impotence. That was an attempt at the positive experiment. Yet it was crude as the belief of certain savages that you'll lift your fighting spirit by eating a human heart. It was probably as false as the pseudoscience of the medieval quack-salvers who recommended the eating of brains for the relief of imbecility.

What good old Doctor Susruta lacked (and would have lacked had he lived till 1929 A.D.) was an organic chemist like University of Chicago's Fred Koch who could have told him that a ton of bull testicles, even when processed chemically, and then taken by mouth, would hardly have sufficed to have given a no-longer-any-good Hindu one night of the good times he'd enjoyed in his youth.

Doctor Newerla points out the shrewdness of the ancient physicians who observed to what a degree the total vitality of men is manufactured in those private laboratories, the testicles. Old Doctor Aretaeus was making his male hormone science in Cappadocia way back in 150 A.D. His description of the vital function of men's sex glands holds, as of today.

"For it is the semen, when possessed of vitality," wrote Aretaeus, "which makes us to be men, hot, well-braced in limbs, well voiced, spirited, strong to think and act." It was the genius of Aretaeus to see that testicles influenced not sex alone, but the total physiology of the human body. "For when the semen is not possessed of its vitality," he said, "persons become shrivelled. . . ."

When you ponder the aging of men, its tragedy, when you remember the deep yen of men to remain well-braced in limbs, spirited, strong to think and act, it seems strange that this fierce instinct for a longer prime of life in itself didn't speed the coming of the hormone hunters and organic chemists. For to the great majority of men, their total vitality must be more precious than life itself. But on the other hand, there's small doubt that this science was stalled for centuries because the tie-up between the testicles and total vitality had an evil, a prurient, an immoral smack to it, especially during the first eighteen centuries A.D. when the ascetic philosophy of Christianity challenged mankind's old pagan and innocent joy in promiscuous fornication.

Let's face it that true Christianity, which together with science may one day lift men above their bestiality, considered the function of the testicles to be not much more than a necessary evil. This is clear when you go to the source, to the sayings of Jesus, as recorded in the Gospel according to St. Matthew, 19: 10, 11, 12. Jesus was laying down the conditions, to his disciples, under which divorce is permissible. And his disciples said: "If the case of a man be so with his wife, it is not good to marry."

Then Jesus told them the high virtue of chastity. "For there are some eunuchs," he said, "which were so born from their mother's womb; and there are some eunuchs, which were made eunuchs of men; and there be eunuchs, which have made themselves eunuchs for the kingdom of heaven's sake. He that is able to receive it, let him receive it."

In short, if a man is *good* enough to take this mutilation, let him take it. And there are thousands of priests, holy men who have tried, and still try, to live as moral eunuchs without mutilation. And there were Russians even down to modern times, that strange sect, the Skoptsi, who actually castrated themselves for the kingdom of heaven's sake. And Count Leo Tolstoy, greatest of all the Russians, throughout his life fought against the fire in his gonads though he was the father of thirteen children, believing to the end of his days that any sexual activity, in or out of wedlock, was evil.

So it is that male hormone science, even if there had been today's organic chemists in the Middle Ages, might well have made small progress. For the pure and innocent yearning of men to remain strong to think and act for many more years than they actually did, it was biological bad luck that nature had put the source of this vigor to so great a degree in men's testicles. Fundamental hormone science had to get its start by the experiments of professors; beyond most men (bankers and clergy excepted) professors are respectable; so this somewhat bawdy experimentation would be conducted by only a few searchers, by men who were so pure in heart that to them the cells of the gonads were on as high a moral level as the cells of the brain, or by men so strong to find scientific truth that they did not give a damn even though sex hormone science was something you didn't mention among the best people.

Whatever the reason, it remains a fact that the quest of the male hormone got a very slow start compared to the study of other parts of our living machinery that has bloomed so brilliantly in the past one hundred and fifty years. At the very early stages of the age of scientific enlightenment, toward the end of the eighteenth century, a French physician, Théophile de Bordeu, made a brilliant prophecy of the profound chemical power that the sex glands exert over the bodies of men. In his book *The Medical Analysis of the Blood*, published the year he died, in 1776, this remarkable medical thinker foretold that the testicles were actually more than mere factories for the manufacture of the sperm, that they were glands that produced an immensely important *internal secretion*.

"The testes give a male tonality to the organism," wrote de Bordeu, ". . . set a seal upon the animalism of the individual. . . . Not only each gland, but each organ of the body, is the workshop of a specific substance or secretion, which passes into the blood, and upon whose secretions the physiological integration of the body as a whole depends."

Théophile de Bordeu foretold today's hormones as being decisive for life or death. "I do not regard these emissions as useless and the result of pure physical necessity or chance;

I rather believe them useful and necessary for the existence of the individual," he wrote.

But for all the inexorably aging men then alive, this was the pity of it, he only wrote it, he didn't try it; he didn't experiment at it so he couldn't prove it. Théophile de Bordeu was physician to the French King Louis XV, and that gay monarch would have paid him well for a new lease on life, would have made no objection to the sexiness of this new science. Right then, the great French scientists, Lavoisier and Laplace, were actually founding experimental biology. They were showing that the quantity of heat which is formed in the body of a warm-blooded animal is equal to that formed in a candle, provided that the quantities of carbon dioxide formed in both cases are identical. By experiment, they were reducing human life to machinery. Right then, Voltaire, Diderot, and D'Alembert were sounding their Encyclopedist's battle cry that all nature and all life could be explained—and transformed!—by experimental science; and they would have loved to go on living to see their dreams come true. But nobody took de Bordeu's theory seriously enough to try to prove it, so it remained mere words added to the millions of words of medical speculation. These lovely words didn't add an hour or a day to the lives of men who wanted to remain hot, spirited, strong to think and act.

CHAPTER ELEVEN

SEVENTY-THREE years went by before any experimenter came to make de Bordeu's prophecy come true, before a man arose to prove experimentally with his hands and his knives that the testicles were living laboratories manufacturing a chemical which then leaked into the blood to keep alive the fire and the fighting strength of an animal's body. This happened in 1849 when the German professor of physiology, Arnold Adolf Berthold, transformed languid capons into fighting roosters.

I know nothing about the personality of this Prometheus of the male sex hormone; his name is not even mentioned in our principal book on medical history by Fielding H. Garrison who was super-conscientious in mentioning all medical great names, true or phony. Berthold was a professor at the University of Göttingen, wrote enormously on a variety of medical subjects. All that's left of him now is a little five page scientific report recording experiments that give him his niche as an immortal in the difficult adventure of extending the prime of life of men.

Berthold simply operated to remove the testicles from four roosters, making them capons. Then he opened the bellies of two of these now sexless birds. Into each of these he planted one testicle. These glands were now in an abnormal position in the bodies of the capons. They had no connection with their former nerve supply. If they worked at all, they'd have to work through the blood. Luck was with Berthold. There was no aseptic surgery in those days, and the capons might well have died as a result of peritonitis from his operation. But they lived. The grafts of the new testicles took. They actually established their blood supply that kept them living in their unnatural location in the capons' bellies.

While the two caponized birds who'd got no testicle grafts became fat pacifists, these other two with the grafted testicles remained every inch roosters. They crowed. They battled. They chased hens enthusiastically. Their bright red combs and wattles kept on growing.

So Berthold, for the first time in history, proved the strength-giving chemistry of the sex glands. Heavily German, Berthold summed up his discovery: "It follows that the present opinion which considers the testes to act upon the blood, and the blood to act correspondingly upon the entire organism—of which the nervous system is an important part—is confirmed."

This simple experiment founded hormone science. Here was a fact so fundamental and powerful that you'd think it would have set medical searchers in full cry on the scent of the male hormone. What was the chemical X in those borrowed sex glands that changed the capons back into roosters? Mind you, it was no longer a futile question as it would have been in the days of old Théophile de Bordeu. Now in the mid-eighteen hundreds there were organic chemists who should have been able to tackle this mystery.

Twenty years before Berthold's experiment, the powerful science of organic chemistry had been founded by the German, Friedrich Wöhler. This genius had actually built up an organic chemical from carbon, hydrogen, oxygen, and nitrogen, constituents of lifeless, inorganic matter. He had synthesized the organic chemical, urea, part of our bodies, hitherto and from the beginning of time only made by nature. In his stills and flasks he had manufactured it without the help of any vital process at all. He had ripped the mystic word "vital" out of the chemistry of all things living. He had founded a chemical faith that there is no real difference between the structural chemistry of life and that of inanimate nature.

Yet so difficult was the new organic chemical science, so haphazard and unconnected the searchings of the hormone hunters on the one hand and the chemists on the other, that, after Berthold, seventy-seven years had to pass—till 1926—before the organic chemists saw even a hint of hope that they might trap the chemical secret of manhood in their laboratories.

In this long interim the fundamental rooster science of Berthold fell upon evil days and came near being discredited altogether. On its basis, a very famous French physiologist, Charles-Edouard Brown-Séquard, claimed that he'd succeeded in making a new man of himself at the age of seventy-two; and the scientific hilarity at Brown-Séquard's imitation of old Ponce de Leon put serious male hormone science on the shelf for many years.

It was not that you could call Brown-Séquard a quack. He was the successor of the celebrated Claude Bernard at the Sorbonne in Paris. In the days immediately after Berthold's rooster experiment, Brown-Séquard himself had made what seemed a landmark advance in the science of other glands of internal secretion. In 1849, in the very year of Berthold's discovery, English Doctor Thomas Addison had described a horribly fatal disease in which people developed a sinister tan, grew thin, grew weaker and weaker till at last they died. They all died. Addison, who is described as a handsome, haughty man of repellent manner, like Osler, had little faith in finding anything to keep really sick people alive; but he made up for that with a great scientific curiosity about what it was that killed them. He cut into the thin, tanned, dead bodies of these victims. They seemed normal—excepting that there was evidence of a sickness of their adrenals, little no-account glands sitting like cocked hats over each kidney.

Now Brown-Séquard made barbarous experiments to prove how these tiny organs (by reason of a chemical something that they must pour into the blood) are decisive for life or death. Having learned expert technique of vivisection from the great Claude Bernard himself, Brown-Séquard now cut those little adrenal glands out of many cats, guinea pigs, rabbits, and dogs who then promptly up and died with a sickness like the human disease discovered by Thomas Addison.

It is now believed that those adrenal-glandless animal martyrs to experimental science—dying far too quickly—actually passed out from shock and infection. But just the same, later more careful experiments proved that Brown-Séquard's idea was right though his experiments were wrong. Animals and men can't live without their adrenal glands; and Brown-Séquard became celebrated as a founder of the science of the glands of internal secretion. Then, with his great prestige, he made the blunder that put the male hormone in the scientific dog house.

It was in 1889, he was getting to be an old man now; and the fires of his doing and his thinking were burning lower and lower. He remembered the rooster experiments of Berthold. He removed the testicles of dogs and guinea pigs. With his mental lights burning dim he mashed up these sex glands and brewed them in a solution of salt. Then he began injecting himself under his skin with this soup made from testicles; and presently, his head held high, a new fire in his eyes, before the great men of French science, Brown-Séquard made an announcement that shook the scientific wide world. He told them that he was rejuvenated, at the age of seventy-two. It is recorded that never before had the ageless quest for perpetual youth been brought so attractively to mankind, nor with as high authority.

"There is a remarkable return of my physical endurance," said Brown-Séquard.

His audience listened spellbound to the news that this testicle soup had brought back his mental power. It had also restored the natural function of his aging bowels.

The poor old scientist's new lease on life lasted about a month, and then he began to wither; and in 1894, he died one of the most discredited searchers in the history of science. He was honest. Before his death he admitted that he likely had fooled himself in that famous experiment. His fine theory spun by the thinking, upper part of his brain, had probably released the acting, lower part of his brain into a final explosion of youthful energy. It was what is called suggestion. It is the arch enemy of scientific truth. It is the almost always false feeling that thousands of varieties of herbs, simples, pills, potions, and serums have stirred up not only in sick people grasping at any straw of hope but also in doctors who imagine they've discovered new remedies.

Now the scientific world broke into a roar of derisive laughter that subsided into sneering snickers that echo down to the present day. Extracts of testicles? Any possible extract of testicles was the bunk and forever. For this blunder his critics now tended to wipe Brown-Séquard off the scientific slate, and completely. They forgot his sound science and the fact that he was a keen thinker. Really he had been ahead of his time and almost certainly correct when he said that the aging process is a progressive *disease* caused by hardening of the arteries. But for this, he was now laughed at by Aldred Scott Warthin who proved himself to be something less than a true scientist by writing that Brown-Séquard lacked the wisdom of David and Solomon in refusing to recognize that the life of man has a definite normal limit—namely three score years and ten.

What was wrong with Brown-Séquard, really, was that he jumped at human experiment too soon. But in the tough world of science (unless you have very heavy financial and scientifico-political backing) you have to be wrong only once to be wrong for always. Even optimists about the power of chemistry over life, like Jacques Loeb, were cruel to the discredited Frenchman.

"Poor Brown-Séquard!" said Loeb. "He injected himself with testicles, ran upstairs, and then died at the top."

In the general sarcastic hilarity Brown-Séquard's sound notion that the sex glands are basic to the maintenance of vigor was forgotten. It is true, as we now know, that he could have injected himself with gallons of his *salt solution* extract of testicles without getting a trace of male hormone under his skin. It is also true that he was unlucky in not trying the right experiments and lazy in not making enough experiments. If he'd only been a bit of an organic chemist, or if he'd team-worked with organic chemists who'd extracted those sex glands with other solvents, with benzene and acetone instead of salt solution, then it might have been poor old Brown-Séquard who had the last laugh. It was his error to be crushed by laughter, but he's to be pardoned because he was so old. It is an error of most men of science, even young ones, that when their first or second or tenth trying of an experiment fails, then their brains tell them it will fail forever.

Now from 1890 onward, hormone hunters didn't forget Brown-Séquard's failure for thirty-seven years. They danced up and down on his scientific grave. They rubbed his mistake into his modest bid for scientific immortality. Maybe what made them so nasty about him, maybe what made the older men of science (who'd all made their own mistakes in less sensational fields) so contemptuous about him was that in their hearts they'd like to have been rejuvenated and were furious at this disappointment.

Whatever the motive, the best of the young hormone hunters wouldn't now touch testicle extracts with a ten-foot pole. While the science of the glands of internal secretion had completely and definitely begun with the testicles of Berthold's rooster, now the thyroids, the adrenals, the pituitary, and the pancreas became the glands of the hour. Even the ovaries, though sexual, were respectable scientifically, maybe because nobody had so far intimated that they might hold the secret of the prolongation of the prime of life in women. But the testicles? Shades of Brown-Séquard, they were a bit too hot to handle. The hormone hunters proceeded to begin to unravel the riddle of the human body's internal chemical control while they pretty much left these disreputable organs out of the picture.

"The unsavory aroma of attempts at rejuvenation," wrote medical historian Gerhard Newerla, somewhat snootily, "did not prevent rapid advances in (other fields of) clinical endocrinology." (My parenthesis.)

What was there really so unsavory about a scientist's attempt to push back old age? Would it have been so odoriferous if he'd experimented with glands other than the testicles? Probably not. Why weren't Pasteur's and Robert Koch's mistakes, made in the unsexual fields of microbe hunting, also unsavory? Why wasn't there a smelliness to the epic series of phony discoveries made by microbe hunter Hideyo Noguchi? Yet nobody was kept from research in yellow fever, Rocky Mountain spotted fever, rabies, and other diseases in which Noguchi had made his historic blunders.

To these dark questions I have no answer. But this was evident, if you were going to experiment upon the secret of vigor hidden in the testicles, you'd better be right, and righter than in any adventure in the whole fight for life. Your experiments would have to be tighter and tougher and more exact, and you'd have to prove yourself right a hundred times over. When any young hormone hunter aspired to tinker chemically with a supposed male hormone, he was as good as licked before he got started. There was the looming danger of the ruin of his career by his becoming scientifically unsavory. This also held for doctors who might try to apply the results of any alleged testicle science to the strengthening of human vigor. It also holds for writers, like the present one, who try to write truly about today's science of the male hormone.

CHAPTER TWELVE

FOR THIRTY-FIVE years after that tragi-comic end of Brown-
Séquard, hormone hunters piled up evidence of a mighty
chemical control of life by other and more respectable glands
of internal secretion. When any gland did have hormonal
activity, which you tested by cutting that gland out of an
animal and watching what happened to him, then it generally
seemed no great chemical trick to prove that the hormone
was there. This brilliant new science mocked the old Frenchman, and seemed to make it more and more doubtful whether
testicles would ever be found to contain any male hormone
at all.

For example, plain dried thyroid gland (you didn't have
to refine it chemically) stoked up the heat-producing power
of dogs and human beings whose fires of life burned low after
removal of their thyroids. Given by mouth, the raw gland
kept low-thyroid children from the dwarfish fate of cretins.
It snapped low-thyroid grown-ups out of the fat-faced, stupid languor of the disease, myxedema. There was plenty of
hormone in the thyroid. Why not then, too, in the testicles,
if they made any hormone at all?

In this gland and that, new hormones seemed to lie on the
surface like nuggets of gold in a scientific El Dorado. The
little adrenal glands, sitting perched like cocked hats above
the kidneys, were full of hormone, and more than one. From
their insides, chemists had no great trouble getting out crystal pure adrenalin that seemed to be useful in flooding our
bodies with emergency vigor needed for fighting or running

away. From the outside layer of these same little glands, the chemists got extracts of another hormone that was actually decisive for life or death; without that hormone men could not live at all.

Now the testicles were far larger than the adrenals; if they did make a male hormone, why shouldn't it be easy to find it?

But the gravest doubt of all seemed to be thrown on old Brown-Séquard's theory of the male hormone by the magic of that truly terrific little gland, the pituitary. Hidden under the brain in the depths of the skull, this tiny organ, hardly bigger than a pea, manufactured maybe a dozen different hormones and seemed to be the master gland of all the body. Here, and not in the testicle, you ought to find the elixir of life, if there was any, and there probably wasn't.

Without the pituitary, animals could not grow; and their thyroid and adrenal glands went out of action; and the testicles and ovaries of young animals failed to develop; and in grown-ups, deprived of the pituitary, their sexual function faded away; and milk dried up in the breasts of nursing animal mothers, and they completely lost their mother love.

The surface experiment of uncovering this amazing variety of hormonal actions was fairly easy. In animals these terrific and fundamental disasters could all be prevented, could even be corrected by implanting pituitary or injecting extracts that the hormone hunters gave in small amounts and that came out of small fractions of an ounce of that tiny gland. So from all this science, it grew to be hormone-hunting orthodoxy that when any gland makes a hormone at all it makes a lot of it. If all these hormones existed so easy to find and in so great an amount in the thyroid, adrenal, and pituitary glands, then it seemed scientifically silly to expect the alleged male hormone to be lurking in the testicles in traces that were next door to infinitesimal. That would be *illogical*. If there were a male hormone, it should come up and hit the first searcher right in the face.

So for thirty-five years those hunters who were willing to make themselves laughingstocks in the scientific world and would risk being whispered about as so many Professor Ponce de Leons, hunters who did have the hardy curiosity to go on looking for this male hormone—looked for it in the scientifically traditional small amount of testicle; they injected small amounts of testicle extracts, and all of them found exactly nothing at all.

Then there arose at the University of Chicago in 1926 a pleasant-faced, mild-mannered, kindly, and extremely modest man with a twinkle in his eye, an organic chemist, Professor Fred C. Koch. He seemed anything but a scientific madcap. He was every inch (externally) the proper professor. He would certainly never aspire to grandstand self-experimentation for perpetual youth. He was highly cultured in the standard and orthodox hormone lore, obedient to the chemical rules, and in no sense hare-brained or illogical; and now (being extremely quiet about it) this gentle Professor Koch set about a fantastic and reckless stewing, extracting, dissolving, fractionating, and distilling of tons of the testicles of bulls— where hormone-hunting chemists before him had worked in ounces.

This was his originality.

To help him with the tremendous chemical skut-work demanded by this forlorn enterprise, Professor Koch had only a young medical student, Lemuel Clyde McGee. Professor Koch showed a curious contempt for seventy-seven years of male hormone failure and negative results and went back to the basic and classical rooster experiment of old Arnold Adolf Berthold. Koch and McGee went back and started all over from scratch and castrated brown leghorn roosters, turning them into capons. Their goal was mad and simple.

If, from their chemical cookery of no matter how many thousands of pounds of bull testicles, they'd find a chemical whisper of something, no matter how tiny, something that would make the wattles and combs of these capons begin to get bright red again, that would make them grow back into the wattles and combs of a regular rooster, well, then they'd know they were on the male hormone's trail.

For the best part of a year they failed among the fumes of ether, benzene, alcohol, acetone, and God-knows-what other chemical solvents. It was like looking for a chemical needle in an endless chemical haystack. It was absolutely without chemical rhyme or reason. It was no brainwork but the crudest kind of cutting and trying; again and again young McGee was down-in-the-mouth and ready to quit in disgust while the gentle Professor Koch kept prodding him. In addition to roosters, they castrated guinea pigs and white rats, watched their prostate glands and seminal vesicles wither away, injected them with this or that and dozens of others among hundreds of chemical fractions out of hundreds of pounds of bull testicles from the near-by stockyards.

Instead of endowing the sexless rats with new vim, vigor, and prostates, many of these infernal extracts actually killed them.

So they failed forward. Koch was of that breed of searchers extolled by Charles F. Kettering who has a low regard for the human brain and a high esteem for what seems to be merely stupid persistence. "The only time you don't want an experiment to fail is the last time you try it!" That is Kettering's grim prescription for scientific success. They ground up bull testicles into mushes, extracted them for five days in 95 per cent alcohol, pressed out those extracts, concentrated them to a sludge under diminished pressure, extracted the sludge with benzene. . . .

And even when they found a bit of power to cause new growth of the combs of capons, the benzene extracts were no good because they caused abscesses in the birds into which they were injected.

They completely removed this nefarious benzene by distilling under diminished pressure and then they treated what was left with acetone; and out of more than forty pounds of original bull testicle, after these epic and stinky stewings, they ended up with a miserable twenty milligrams—less than one-thousandth of an ounce—of acetone-soluble material. Now here was a capon with its combs and wattles mere shadows of its former proud roosterhood; and into this fat and placid bird they injected one milligram of this material each day and for days nothing happened, and for weeks they kept up their foolish injections till one day, shades of poor old Brown-Séquard, Lemuel Clyde McGee and Fred Koch both had to admit it.

The comb and the wattles of that capon were actually turning brighter, redder. *The comb of that capon was growing.*

They did it all over with all the care of a good housewife following her rule exactly to make all her pumpkin pies come out just so; and it happened again and again, which is all there is to sound science really, this being able to duplicate the results you got the first time when you do the same experiment, every pernickety step of it, exactly over and over. So Koch and Lemuel Clyde McGee could now look each other in the eye and shake hands solemnly and tell each other that, by treating bull testicles with benzene, and then with acetone, just so, you arrived at a something, an X, chemically mysterious, but a definite something that contained, in a high state of impurity, but just the same contained, the male hormone.

Now Professor Koch revealed his kindliness and modesty. It was young McGee who had done the dirty work. It was McGee who had burned his hands and worked red-eyed into the night. So now Lemuel Clyde McGee (acknowledging the "assistance" of Doctor Fred C. Koch) alone under his own name published a little scientific paper that should have shaken the world of science but didn't. It was entitled enigmatically and with every care to avoid sensationalism: "The Effect of the Injection of a Lipoid Fraction of Bull Testicle in Capons."

Long after these present pages have crumbled and have vanished into oblivion, Lemuel Clyde McGee will be known in the immortal archives of science as the man who first proved that there actually was a male hormone.

Having at this tender age as a mere medical student carved out his immortal niche, McGee resumed his medical studies and vanished from the hormone picture. Was it possible the male hormone might now die a-bornin'?

The money for the bull testicles, gallons of chemicals, guinea pigs, rats, and roosters had been donated by the famous pharmaceutical House of Squibb. If Koch and McGee could get out a workable male hormone this might be bread cast upon the waters. How many millions of American males, not the men they used to be, would flock to the physicians and the druggists, a bit shame-faced and surreptitious, maybe, but hopeful, murmuring: "Doc, how about some of this new male hormone?"

But now that the first hint of that hormone had been trapped, the House of Squibb withdrew its support. Who could blame them? The executives were sensible men. If it took all this chemical time, toil, and sweat to get a little bit of a mysterious something out of the testicles of so many bulls, just enough of it to bring a few capons back to rooster-hood, what was the percentage, when was the pay-off?

To these sound businessmen it seemed clear that Koch was as far from a profitable drugstore article as the first tamer of fire had been from a practical steam engine. So to the firm of Squibb must go the restricted honor of having made the beginning of this wild adventure possible; it was like furnishing one lone explorer ten pounds of pemmican, one sledge, and six husky dogs to go from Labrador to the North Pole. But Fred Koch was in his gentle way of the stern stuff that

Amundsen and Stefansson are made of. He realized full well the impropriety of asking the authorities of the University of Chicago to back a science with such ultimately sexy implications. It was broad-minded enough of them that they allowed him to work at it. But he kept asking around for money.

The help came from a University of Chicago biologist of the utmost respectability and distinction. Professor Frank R. Lillie had long been interested in those sad female calves known as freemartins. They are female calves born as twins to males. They are sterile, absolutely barren. It was Professor Lillie's profoundly worked-out theory that in the cow mother's womb, by way of their joined-up blood circulation, the male hormone of the unborn bull calf invaded the body of his unborn twin sister and knocked out all future possibility of her ever becoming a mother.

Now if Fred Koch was actually trapping the male hormone (which had been purely theoretical and non-existent) you could test out this theory of the unfortunate freemartins. There was nothing raffish about such a scientific enterprise. It brought back no echoes of Ponce de Leon. It wouldn't jeopardize the sexless dignity of the great university. Professor Lillie would sponsor Fred Koch's academically very ticklish adventure. So now the grave and sexually impeccable Committee for Research in Problems of Sex of the National Research Council—the very Vatican of American science—advanced a modest sum of research money that sent Fred Koch back to his stewing of bull testicles with bright new hope.

When the records are all in, when scientific sagas are intoned in the Valhalla to which all good searchers will go, this will be remembered about Fred Koch: that he didn't give a damn how pitifully little male hormone there was in any given vast quantity of testicle so long as he could prove that there was any hormone there at all. This made him completely impractical. Because if the male hormone existed in the body as a will-o'-the-wisp, how could any sane man give it importance as the maker of manhood? But there is a contrary and practical quirk about Fred Koch that will be told in the searcher's Valhalla. He would not rest till he got that hormone so pure, so devoid of poisonous contaminations that it would be harmless even though you injected it in huge doses.

This was inspired horse sense, for what good is a hormone that restores roosterhood (or manhood) if it kills the capon (or the eunuch) in the process? The discovery of life-saving insulin had been delayed all of twelve years because the first pancreas hormone extracts were toxic.

So Fred Koch, now aided by Doctor T. F. Gallagher, went back at a super-purification. In their laboratory they tackled this acetone-soluble hint of what makes bulls bulls. They purified it further with the solvent, hexane, then shook it with alcohol, then washed the alcohol layer five times with hexane, then re-extracted this hexane stuff twice again with alcohol, then again washed each alcohol layer five times with hexane, and then proceeded to transfer the material, soluble in alcohol, to ether, and shook it with alkali till it dissolved and then shook that solution five times again with ether and then shook that ether solution repeatedly with water.

Till you'd swear that, after such an appalling chemical shoving around, whatever chemical will-o'-the-wisp remained, would have forgotten that it ever had come from the gonad of a bull.

This was mere Teutonic thoroughness. Now surely if there was anything left of the male hormone at all, it should be by this time devoid of all contaminating chemicals, it should be the real hormone McCoy. But, no. Not for our professor. "The product is as yet grossly impure," wrote Koch. "We should not yet give it a name, too little is known of its chemistry. A chemical name would give us a false sense of security as regards the purity of our product."

But, presto, this chemical manhandling had enormously increased the hormone's power. Now instead of its taking some weeks of injections to make a capon somewhat roosterish, now one hundredth of a milligram, one three-millionth of an ounce, injected once a day for just five days, began to endow capons with evidence of male adornment, and with a promise of the rooster's gallant song, and fight, and vigor.

By 1929, T. F. Gallagher and Fred C. Koch (Koch's name second as usual) dared to publish in cold scientific print without the customary timid scientific hedging that here at last was the testicular hormone. It exerted not only in capons but in castrated guinea pigs and rats all the biological effects thus far proposed for a male hormone if such a chemical actually did exist.

Again Fred Koch showed a curious modesty, a lack of that arrogance and ambition for glory that drives on even the best of searchers. He had pointed out a precise chemical road. He had opened up a broad trail through the jungle of thousands of chemicals that hid the hormone in the testicle. He was set for the final attack. He seemed within grasp of the ultimate honor, the actual isolation of the elixir of manhood in a crystal-pure condition. That would make the world's chemists kowtow. That would put Koch in line for the Nobel Prize. That would put Koch on the front pages of newspapers. Now he should hoard these precious final extracts, should work at them in the breath-taking excitement of watching for the ultimate pure crystals to form out of the final solution. It was like being within one day's climb from the top of Mt. Everest.

But Fred Koch was not the man to hoard his science. He was a coöperator, not a prima donna. He was a hint of the anonymous team-working man of science of the future.

At the University of Chicago there was excitement, obscure and academic, about this manhood Koch had trapped in a test tube. The hubbub was not about what this might mean for men, but what it might portend for animal hormone science. Chicago's biologist, Doctor Carl R. Moore, had made brilliant experiments showing that the testicles are not self-controlled organs. The little pituitary gland up under the brain had a big part in maintaining the reproductive system as a going unit. But on the other hand, when you castrated a rat, the loss of its testicles had a queer effect upon the pituitary so that, though you might say the pituitary dominated the activity of the testicles, still the testicles also had a chemical say-so over the pituitary. It was a sort of chemical, hormonal tit-for-tat.

Fred Koch was glad to give Professor Moore large amounts of his preciously little highly purified male hormone; and Moore's rat experiments seemed to show that when you injected rats with the male hormone, then the power of their pituitary glands to stimulate sex glands went down remarkably. All this in the quaint, abstruse world of the professors was very intriguing. But it meant just that much less chance for Koch to do his fundamental chemist's duty, to get to his ultimate chemist's goal, namely to purify this male hormone down to its final crystalline form, so that he could write the hieroglyphic diagram of its organic chemical structure, and the precise number of carbon, hydrogen, and oxygen atoms of its chemical formula.

If he could do that, then, maybe, who knew, it might be possible to make tons of this elixir that was so rare in the gonads of bulls.

But now scientific medical men came to him also wanting more and more of Fred Koch's precious stock of the powerful, but still impure and chemically mysterious, male hormone. These medical scientists, mind you, were not crackpots like old Brown-Séquard on the trail of perpetual youth. They were demanding the answer to a most fundamental scientific question. Would this male hormone that had such a magic effect upon capons and castrated rats have any action at all upon certain unfortunate human beings? These were called eunuchoids. They were the kind of people "born eunuchs in their mother's womb," in the words of the Bible.

Could Professor Koch furnish him with, let's say, fifty days' supply of his male hormone, asked Professor A. T. Kenyon.

Would Koch's brew do for eunuchoids, human, what it did for capons? Here in Professor Kenyon's clinic was a twenty-six-year-old man, or an almost-man, it would be more accurate to call him. At the age of fourteen he had developed a little pubic hair, but since that time he had made no manly progress. His voice was childish. Every two weeks he pathetically shaved a bit of fuzz off his upper lip and his chin. He had experienced only the feeblest of sexual sensations, and these were very rare, and he had never had a discharge of sperm. The X rays showed that his long bones had not developed like those of a grown-up. His testicles were tiny and his basal metabolism was low.

For fifty-three days in succession this almost-man was given injections of the male hormone. No, it was not harmful in the slightest; there were no abscesses or local reactions. But in this child of twenty-six, events took place that were hopeful and momentous and yet a little sad. As the injections continued, for the first time in his life, this boy who could not seem to grow up began to feel the hot surge of real sexual drive; and it was not in his mind only, but there was the most striking evidence of it physically, measurably, or, as the scientists say, objectively. During the period of these daily hormone injections he became in a sexual sense like a strong and normal youth. For the first time in his life he experienced, and repeatedly, the sexual climax of the ejaculation of semen. Then came the day when that precious male hormone extract was exhausted; there wasn't a drop more of it in Koch's laboratory.

So the experiment ended; and this human experimental animal who had been brought to the threshold of a belated manhood felt his borrowed virility fade away.

This first human test of the male hormone was historic and ridiculous. To give this almost-man a first hint of what drives normal men to mating, those fifty-three injections had used up the total male hormone from more than half a ton of bull's testicles!

This was as wildly impractical as any experiment in medical history. It surely justified the horse sense of those pharmaceutical manufacturers who decided that male sex hormone research was not the place to invest your money. This new male hormone's power to awaken a dormant sexual springtime was wonderful, but at this rate not even old John D. Rockefeller, Sr., would be able to afford it. It seemed really the feeblest scientific step ahead of the hoax perpetrated by old Brown-Séquard. Looking at it as a realistic biologist you could even question any significance of this will-o'-the-wisp of elixir that Fred Koch had stewed out of so many tons of testicles over a period of seven years with such devotion and chemical skill. Since this hormone was present in such tiny traces in tons of gonads, could you really call it the cause of bovine bulldom?

If you'd have to keep on extracting such a next-to-nothing out of so many tons of bull glands, what could it possibly promise as a spark of new life for run-down human machinery?

These pessimistic questions were enough to discourage the most optimistic biologists and doctors. They were enough to dishearten anybody—certain organic chemists excepted.

CHAPTER THIRTEEN

When trying to master the fundamental facts of any branch of medical science, it's my habit to go back to the very first beginnings and work forward, paying no mind during this time to the last brilliant consequences as of today.

This is good discipline. I don't know that I've achieved it to perfection—for instance, I may have been too hard on the famous physician, Osler. According to the lights of his time, according to the state of knowledge then, his pessimism may have been justified. Trying to keep to the discipline of the calendar, at times I doubted this search, deeply. If at the time of Fred Koch's getting that first sex urge going in that eunuchoid man, with such a faint whisper of impure hormone from eleven hundred pounds of bull glands, if I'd then stopped digging into the deeds of the hormone hunters, I'd have been convinced that it was absolutely chimerical to hope for a practical male hormone to revigorate men. The will-o'-the-wisp of elixir that it had taken Fred Koch seven years to extract from tons of bull's testicles remained chemically mysterious; it was worth many times its weight in gold; it seemed destined to stay a laboratory curiosity for the amusement of hormone hunters whose interests were academically sexual.

Yet Herman Bundesen's enthusiasm kept urging me on. "They've got it now," he said. "Look, you've got only as far as 1933!"

Herman Bundesen re-stoked my curiosity because look at him, here in 1943 he was nearly 62 and tanned and tough and taut and vigorous as if he were going to go on living forever. God knows no other medical men of my acquaintance were talking about the male hormone. It was only Bundesen and his courage that shamed me into going ahead with the history of testosterone, step by step. He made me believe that this new male hormone, though no key to perpetual youth, was at least a chemical cog that was vital to our human machinery. Bundesen's optimism fired me to believe that a disease-free mankind was more than a dream, that it might soon become the goal of the boldest leaders of public health and medical research. He kept dinning it into me that there was no irreducible minimum to any human death rate.

"Wasn't Pasteur right when he prophesied that all microbic plagues could be wiped off the globe?" asked Herman.

"I'll admit Pasteur would have had the right to foretell it, if public health had a hundred Bundesens," I said.

He brushed off this compliment, looked far into the future, assumed every damned dirty deadly microbe had been wiped off the earth. "Now the chemists suspect that growing old simply isn't natural," said Bundesen.

"You're not telling me they're going to make us immortal," I offered.

"No, but they're suspecting that growing old *the way we do now* is really only another disease," he said.

Herman Bundesen was futuristic, all right. He showed me how our hospitals, today, are mere repairshops to patch up damaged human machines that we manhandle through our ignorance during our whole lives so that those machines usually creak to a stop before they reach seventy. But tomorrow? Tomorrow our chemists and engineers would join up with the doctors to transform these dingy stinking hospitals into laboratory-health centers, gleaming workshops to build a brand-new humanity that on the average might live at top total vitality far beyond one hundred years.

"Don't sell these new organic chemists short," warned Bundesen.

I went away from Herman Bundesen, so strong and youthful amid the physically down-at-heel appearance of the vast majority of men of his age in Chicago. I went back to the sun house at Wake Robin, back to digging through hundreds of scientific publications in German, French, and English on the history of hormone hunters groping up the trail toward testosterone. I woolgathered looking out to the horizon line where the pale blue lower western sky met the dark blue water and remembered back to my young microbe-hunting days, when I'd met my first organic chemist, at Ann Arbor, Michigan.

This was a little Jewish man, Professor Moses Gomberg, not only one of the greatest organic chemists in the world (still living) but the most wonderful teacher I had ever known. In his thick accent, which his gentle voice made charming, he reduced the living world, all living beings whose complexity so befuddled the doctors, to the comparative simplicity of the structural formulas of organic chemicals.

"I had thought once of becoming a physician," Gomberg told me, "but the trouble is, to medical science there is no rime or reason."

The rationality of medical science would come only when the organic chemists took hold of it. Gomberg would show me queer models, little balls with different colors representing, each color, atoms of carbon, oxygen, hydrogen, nitrogen, sulfur and so on, all arranged in space, stuck on the ends of wires, looking like three dimensional Chinese puzzles. These were the molecules of organic chemicals; these were the chemist's imagination of chemical structures so tiny that the then best microscope and the keenest eye would never detect them. But the magical thing was that Gomberg and his strange new ilk of men could prove that these molecules actually existed. They stewed, extracted, cooked, distilled not only coal tar but the blood, the tissues, the protoplasm of plants and animals and men. Amid fumes of alcohol, ether, benzene, and a dozen other solvents they stood before their laboratory benches like so many sorcerer's apprentices. They burned themselves. They were undaunted by explosions. They were not stopped by a thousand failures in their drive to find pure organic chemicals that might mean the precise difference between life and death. In Gomberg's days, when I worshipped him between 1909 and 1920, in this quest they had got next to nowhere.

But this was the gleaming hope that Gomberg showed me. By infinitely patient super-cookery they could start with comparatively simple organic compounds, put on an oxygen atom, hook it to this carbon on their imaginary molecule models, take off a hydrogen atom from that one, stick in a sulfur atom here, add a nitrogen atom there, and if they only stuck to it, if they only kept the chemical faith, they'd make in their laboratories every one of the millions, maybe billions, of organic chemical compounds that were the building blocks of all living things.

In Gomberg's own great days thirty years ago, the organic chemists had only the most modest successes; their main achievements were with coal-tar dyes; they had done almost nothing to give medical research that rime or reason that Gomberg said it lacked so lamentably. Their one microbe-fighting victory was that of salvarsan concocted by gay old Paul Ehrlich and the German chemist, Bertheim, who was later killed by one of his explosions. And even that chemical victory was Pyrrhic, because salvarsan's arsenic was almost as deadly to men as it was to the syphilis spirochete itself that tried to kill them.

But now look what had happened since those primitive organic chemical days! In this last tragic and magic decade between 1933 and 1943 the organic chemists had at last come into their own. A most marvelous fireworks of world-changing, life-giving discovery shot up out of their laboratories in

Europe and America. In these past ten years they worked as if in a grim race with death. They toiled for a better world and a stronger mankind as if in apology for their organic chemist forerunners who had invented T.N.T. and the poison gas, which in the hands of today's destroyers and haters of life, now threatened the wiping out of civilization and maybe of all humanity. They worked as if they must hurry, hurry, because there was so little time, what with death brooding so menacingly over mankind.

In the past ten years compared to us ordinary people and even to physicians these new organic chemists were a new breed of men. They were making wood stronger than steel; inventing glass softer than silk; concocting super-fuels that would send airplanes almost vertically up into the sky and to any part of the world in fifty hours; finding materials for comfortable six-room houses that you could put on a trailer and set up wherever you wanted to live. They began to dazzle the doctors, discovering new organic substances that promised to wipe malignant microbes out of the world where before they've been combatted mainly by the bedside manner. They synthesized chemicals that would cause cancer and calmly predicted other chemicals that would cure it.

I left off woolgathering and went back digging at the curious, furtive history of testosterone. Yes, Herman Bundesen was absolutely right, I must not sell these chemical wizards short.

Within three years after that time in 1933 when Fred Koch's male hormone was so will-o'-the-wisp and seemed so medically impractical, the organic chemists had given the laugh to my gloomy predictions.

From Fred Koch's laboratory the news that there was actually a male hormone hiding in his testicular gunk—which is organic chemist's slang for impure material—though still very impure and chemically unknown, had jumped the ocean to Europe. Out of twenty-five thousand liters of male human urine the German chemist Adolf Butenandt trapped a whisper of pure crystals that showed male hormone activity, starting capons back toward roosterhood.

Again it seemed really a silly experiment, and not only because so little hormone came from such oceans of urine, but also because these pure crystals hadn't a tenth of the power of the impure gunk that Fred Koch had got from the bull testicles. Which was the real male hormone, if any?

. Butenandt was undaunted. He determined the exact chemical formula of those crystals. Then, more portentous, he could write down the hieroglyphic diagram, he could build a model that gave the exact structural arrangement of their carbon, hydrogen, and oxygen atoms in space. It was not the same male hormone Fred Koch had found in bull's testicles, because treatment with alcohol and alkali failed to kill it. But now the organic chemists could add something to it here, take off a bit there. Sure as shooting they'd transform the pure but feeble power of those crystals into a hormone as strong as Koch's or maybe more powerful than he'd ever dreamed of.

Then the clues in the hormone hunt, so far so intangible, began at last to click together. In the summer of 1935, organic chemists in the laboratory of the German Jewish pharmacologist, Ernst Laqueur, in Amsterdam in Holland actually got a hormone out of bull's testicles, acting in every way chemically like Fred Koch's original, but now crystal pure. Wonderful! A measly smidge of one one-hundred-and-fiftieth of an ounce of powerfully acting hormone crystals out of one ton of testicles! Laqueur's hormone crystals were just a bit chemically different, but definitely different from the crystals Butenandt had got out of that twenty-five thousand quarts of urine. And they were many more times powerful than Butenandt's in changing capons back into fighting, romantic roosters.

The Dutch chemists quickly determined the precise struc-

tural arrangement of their powerful hormone crystals. They
were sure now they had the real male hormone trapped
chemically; and they gave it the lovely-sounding and faintly
sexual name—"testosterone."

Though this was beyond hardly a doubt the true male
hormone, yet it remained impractical, existing as it did in the
bull gonads in such a faint whisper.

In that very same summer of 1935, the Jugoslav chemical
genius Leopold Ružička in Zurich, Switzerland, turned the
chemical, cholesterol (that's found in every cell of the living
bodies of animals and human beings) into synthetic testosterone.

Now at last the hormone hunt was over. Now the organic
chemists were in. Now here was abundant raw material to
make testosterone. Now forget about bull testicles. You could
get limitless cholesterol from the brains and spinal cords of
cattle.

Here within three years was an international chemical
miracle. Where in 1933 Fred Koch was finding tiny fractions
of ounces of impure and utterly impractical male hormone
in tons of bull testicles, now Ružička (with Butenandt
quickly confirming him) could calmly predict the artificial
manufacture of tons of pure testosterone. That could be predicted in 1936.

At this triumphant moment of my digging in the records
of the hormone hunt I became gloomy again.

What now about the doctors? Among them it had aroused
no medical furore when Fred Koch's traces of impure male
hormone had awakened a bit of a sexual urge in that first
lone eunuchoid man. But what magic—beneficent, bawdy, or
dangerous—would be made by medical men with the possible
powerful injections of the vast amounts of this pure synthetic
testosterone that would presently be in their hands?

The answer to this momentous question was decidedly iffy.
I knew my doctors pretty well; and though they were sup-

posed to be coldly scientific in their knowledge of sexual activities, they would probably blush and become as confused as the ordinary citizen at the prospect that the sexual vigor of worn-out men, ordained by God to vanish as men grew older, might possibly be renewed by any chemical, including testosterone. Could doctors, even the best of them, be expected to test out the power of the new synthetic male hormone, openly, impartially?

Of course the best doctors, the few who had some smattering of chemical knowledge, knew that testosterone was *chemically* respectable. The brilliant feat of its synthesis was causing scientific excitement, and Ružička and Butenandt were already being mentioned as almost sure for the Nobel Prize which they were later awarded. But here was the rub. Testosterone, for all that it was now made in chemical kettles, was sexy. Experiment with it upon human beings would be a bit bawdy. I had sat with many an eminent medical research committee. I could hear the doctors now presented with the chance to test the new male hormone on broken men and worn-out men.

"Dynamite, gentlemen, it's pure dynamite," I could hear them mutter.

Your best doctor is as moral and as hypocritical as the next man. Pondering over testosterone's possible fantastic power now that it could be injected in huge doses (animal experiments were showing it was not poisonous) I didn't blame the eminent doctors of the medical committees for their timidity. The distinguished doctors of the councils that hold the scientific purse strings for research were the first to realize they'd got hold of a possibly two-edged sword. There was already enough fornicatory trouble in our increasingly immoral world among young gentlemen and ladies who had too much natural male and female hormone. It would be a better world if the doctors could only find ways to put a lot of that natural hormone on ice.

I could see the heads of medical research puzzled and worried. If testosterone had upon men the terrific effect hormone hunters were proving it to have on capons, and if it got loose commercially among human beings, what kind of spectacle would human oldsters make of themselves, with their banked sexual fires flaring again, with them prancing about under testosterone's hot influence?

I could not blame the eminent citizens of the scientific research committees if they'd go very easy with this new sexual T.N.T.

Mind you, I was not at this moment in these ponderings living in today, 1944. Mentally I was back in 1936 when testosterone first made its somewhat raffish bow to a few scientific men in the know in the medical world. At this time in 1936, not only testosterone, but also the newly synthesized chemically pure B-vitamins, and even the sulfas and the new pure *female* hormone, estrone, all of them were chemical upstarts. They were new-fangled. I remembered back to the brave days of the microbe-hunting discoveries of Pasteur and Robert Koch, to the kind of bum's rush the most authoritative doctors had given these microbes that were supposed to be so murderous. Could any of these new chemicals (and most of all testosterone) be so decisive for feebleness or strength as the famine fighters and the hormone hunters claimed?

In the mid nineteen-thirties the organic chemists were still intruders, they were suspicious characters in the world of medical practice. I knew hundreds of doctors, I had taken a kind of cross-section test of what they considered their duty and goal as physicians. And in 1936 the great majority of them, from the best specialists to the garden variety pill-peddler and layer-on-of-hands, were patchers of life, and did not aspire to be its transformers. When I spoke of a new humanity—à la Herman Bundesen—these doctors looked at me sympathetically and as if to say, "Paul, you're crazy."

To these excellent physicians in 1936, my new heroes, the organic chemists, seemed a combination of men from Mars and ancient Rosicrucians—too miraculous. The physicians, God bless them, and especially the more honest and hard-boiled among them, were skeptical of chemical miracles because in the middle nineteen-thirties they had not experienced them.

The famine fighters with their pure crystal thiamin, riboflavin, and ascorbic acid and these hormone hunters with their estrone and testosterone seemed suspect to the best doctors. To the physicians, the famine-fighting and hormone-hunting chemists seemed a bit too bold in their project to improve upon God. From time's beginning God had made men almost perfect, in his own image, yet destined to crack up in mid-life and wear out before three score and ten. To these new-fangled chemists, life was not sacred, mortality was not inevitable, life was a combination of benzene rings and hydrocarbons; and death was only a chemical accident.

I couldn't blame the doctors, few of whom knew one simple organic compound from another, for scoffing at the wild dreams of a few organic chemists in 1936 who after all knew nothing about the human body the way the doctors knew it. I confess, having put myself back among these new chemical vitamins and hormones as they made their bow in the middle nineteen-thirties, that I, too, though not having the ancient wisdom of doctors, thought the organic chemists were slightly crazy.

Here they were claiming that these new vitamins and hormones were *key chemicals of life*. They actually aspired to disentangle, out of the millions of complex chemical compounds that make up the human body, a few vital chemicals that might give the answer to what makes men weak and what keeps them strong, what lets men live and what makes them die. In 1936 they were already theorizing, on the ground of certain experiments with capons, castrated and starving rats and famished and sexless guinea-pigs, that a lack or a waning of these few chemical vitamins and hormones might account for God-knows-what enigmatic diseases, for the waning of human vigor, for the early onrush of old age itself.

To me, as well as to the doctors, all this seemed a bit thick if not downright ridiculous; and testosterone (most of all because of its rejuvenating possibilities) was going to have tough sledding among the physicians.

But then in that very year, 1936, began the series of chemical miracles (having nothing whatever to do with the male hormone) that made the organic chemists medically respectable and more, the trail-blazers of all new medical progress, the agitators of a revolution in the fight for life.

The master medical discovery of the century turned out to be pioneered by a chemically dabbling youngster who was no doctor at all. The name of this boy in his early twenties is recorded as having been P. Gelmo, of Vienna. Way back in 1908 this downy stripling of organic chemistry had put together, synthesized, a curious organic chemical compound that did not exist in nature, that seemed not to have been thought of even by God. This was para amino benzene sulfonamide. It had taken the doctors twenty-four years to discover that this first sulfa drug of Gelmo's was the most powerful microbe-destroyer ever discovered, bringing back from the grave women who were inexorably dying of child-bed fever.

Then the organic chemists got to work on this first sulfa that the now forgotten Gelmo had prepared merely as a classroom exercise; successively and within four years they chemically transformed it into more and more death-smashing, life-saving sulfapyridine, sulfathiazole, sulfadiazine; and by 1940 the organic chemists had completely stunned and bedazzled the medical world. These sulfas were justly lumped under the mystic nickname, God's powder. They gave the humblest backwoods doctor or surgeon in Keokuk or Novo-Sibirsk a dominion over malignant microbic death that from time's beginning had defied the most learned and expensive specialist physicians and surgeons.

In less than a half-dozen years' time, the organic chemists had so revolutionized medicine that the death-fighting power of the medical profession, from high to low, was far more than doubled. (Today, for example, in our country though 50,000 doctors, half of all our physicians, are off to the wars, the civilian death rate has increased very little, and the health of the nation stays pretty steady, though only the older and the 4-F doctors are left to take care of us.)

Now in the eyes of the doctors the organic chemists were transformed from perpetrators of laboratory stinks into life-saving leaders, magicians. The sulfas were joined as human death fighters by the little yellow pills of another organic chemical, atabrine. This new drug (plus mosquito control) promised to wipe out of every civilized land, malaria, mankind's master-destroyer that sickened an estimated eight hundred million people yearly and killed between five and ten million.

Pondering all this and realizing the effect of miracles upon men when those miracles are actual, I could see why it was that by 1940, in regard to these crazy chemists the doctors were beginning to pipe a different tune. In a few years these wizards of the stills and chemical kettles had made possible the saving of more human life than all the doctors with their knives and pills and herbs and simples and kindly bedside manner had saved in all human history.

I saw that this might make the more progressive physicians a bit more open-minded about vitamins and hormones, maybe even testosterone. If these chemists could discover key chemicals that jangled the life machinery of microbes so that they were no longer deadly, were they so crazy claiming they already had other chemicals that were vital cogs in the machine of the human body?

Here was the B-vitamin, thiamin, absolutely decisive for life or death. No tree, no fish, no bird, no dog, no snake, no baby could develop and grow without it. Here was the further B-vitamin, riboflavin, helping thiamin to stoke up those oxidations inside of every living human cell, those oxidations that old Jacques Loeb had said were the difference between living and dying. Here was nicotinic acid, absolutely necessary to the working of the human brain. These crystal-pure vitamins all made their bow on the stage in the drama of life or death in those same fateful years along with the sulfas.

Here was their miracle. These synthetic chemicals, shot in huge doses into human beings who were nervous, calmed them; who were dying, resurrected them; who were in deep dementia, made them sane; who were going blind, made them see. These were the miracles that the pure vitamin chemicals made *in people who were found to lack them*.

Among people who were chemically starved for them, they behaved exactly like keys unlocking doors slammed shut against life.

It was not only the synthetic vitamins that revealed life-restoring power. The female hormone, estrone, was the most curiously close chemical cousin to the male hormone, testosterone. This estrone had got the medical jump on testosterone, probably because it didn't have testosterone's disreputable pretensions of perpetual youth. Estrone began showing the doctors its power to calm the nervous torture and to cure even the insanity of many women at the time of their change of life.

All these chemicals, respectable and powerful, set the stage for the medical trial of testosterone, despite its disreputable original natural site of origin in the bulls. To the biologists— to whom nothing is naughty—testosterone, now that it was pure and abundant, was revealing an absolutely fantastic power. Injected into pregnant female rats, it changed their girl babies toward boys in the rat mother's womb. It speeded up the tempo of developing life outlandishly. It could make male baby roosters crow within sixty hours after they were hatched from the egg.

In its crystals hormone hunters discovered facts a bit beyond the natural.

In a series of experiments made by zoologists at the University of Chicago, testosterone showed a weird effect not only on roosters or capons, but pullets. These serious scientists were engaged in a deep study of what they called the social order of flocks of hens. They sat watching the conduct of flocks of hens in cages and made marks in their notebooks solemnly recording which hens pecked at what other hens, which pecked most consistently and viciously. They established that there are definitely hens who are queens of the roost and other hens who are so many Mrs. Caspar Milquetoasts. They recorded that the best hen-peckers are at the top of the social scale.

And, by the beard of Charles Darwin, testosterone, given to the timid chickens, could cause them to upset the hereditary superiority and challenge the social championship of the most bellicose biddies. Testosterone turned formerly timid pullets into fighters dauntless as Jack Dempsey.

Joking aside (and this science was exact and serious, mind you), testosterone, when you gave enough of it, could actually transform hens towards roosters. They stopped laying eggs; their hinder parts narrowed towards the anatomical build of that of their lords and masters; they started to strut; they began to crow; they conducted themselves in every particular like kings of the barnyard—though they might not become actual fathers.

When you stopped injecting testosterone, they relapsed to henhood. Yes, sex is chemical and the male sex chemical seemed to be the key not only to sex but to enterprise, courage and vigor.

What would testosterone do for men in the hands of the doctors? They could now ignore its having been discovered in testicles and regard it as a steroid compound, originating in chemical kettles. What would the pure male hormone do for certain almost-men and certain broken men, eunuchoids who'd been deprived of their own natural hormone from birth or by disease or accident? Would it stir the fire of their total vitality; would it make them strong to think and act?

PART III

THE RESCUE OF BROKEN MEN

CHAPTER FOURTEEN

A TWENTY-SEVEN-YEAR-OLD boy, you couldn't truly call him a man, told his miserable half-life to physicians at the Medical College in Albany, New York. For many years he had suffered migraine headaches; he experienced hot flashes like a middle-aged woman; for years, after not much physical exertion, he had tired like an old man; he felt vague discomforts and distresses; and especially he complained that he was ashamed to live. The Albany Medical College doctors did not know what to do for him; his tragic condition was idiopathic, which was the medical impressive word for describing utter ignorance of what caused it. His sad boyishness and his physical feebleness were "of the nature of an idiopathy; self-originated; neither sympathetic nor traumatic." This learned description did not help him. His state appeared to be hereditary, and who could improve on an incompleteness wished upon him by God? The doctors admitted themselves powerless, but there was one member of the Albany Medical College faculty who was willing to take a real stab in the dark at helping him.

This was James B. Hamilton, a teacher of anatomy who held the mere degree of Ph.D. and, therefore, did not have the legal right to prescribe any medicine for this sad boy's condition, nor to dose him. Indeed, in the most official medical circles the degree of Ph.D. does not rate the title of "Doctor," that prefix being reserved for M.D.'s, dentists, and veterinarians, which latter are usually called "Doc." Just the same, anatomist James B. Hamilton had a theory that he could

91

chemically boost this boy toward manhood; and to sanctify and legalize the experiment he was now about to undertake he called into coöperation Doctors Eldridge Campbell, Judson Gilbert, John Heslin, Harry Tebbutt, Joseph Schwind, and Harold Himwich. These medical men are to be remembered, not only for taking part in an historic experiment, but also because they would follow the lead of a man who, though an anatomist, was only a member of what the doctors call the laity.

If this obscurely epochal event in the history of testosterone in 1937 were now being told aloud in the intimacy of a circle of listeners before the log fire at Wake Robin where visitors usually have a strong scientific bent, even then I should have to ask all who consider sex and its mysteries to be the least bit shameful or sinful, please, at this point, to leave the room. So now I must warn all readers who blush at the facts of sex either to skip this chapter in the history of testosterone—or better even to stop reading the book altogether. Because from here on out, if the story is to make any sense at all, the plainest talk will be unavoidable. The events about to be described cannot be told in the kindergarten terms of the story of the love lives of the birds, the bees, and the flowers.

It is not that James B. Hamilton's experiment had lewd motives. His scientific austerity is so unquestioned that he has since been promoted to the medical faculty of Yale University. Anatomist Hamilton's experiment was based upon the coldly scientific fact that all the parts of the human body, private or public, have an equal dignity and importance. If I'm going to have to use words now that cause shudders among polite people, I can only plead that the theme of the story of the male hormone is primarily *not* sexual.

What concerns us here is a question as old as humanity. Is or is not the total vitality of men tied up with their sexual vigor? And has science now developed to the state where this question can be answered, yes or no? And if the answer is yes, then have the organic chemists and the hormone hunters brought us to the point where men whose total vitality is slipping can begin to have some hope for a new lease on life?

This twenty-seven-year-old boy who came complaining to the Albany physicians was himself a medical student and intelligent and industrious. It was only when fully clothed that he might pass for a man. His hips were wide like a woman's; he had protruding breasts like a girl's; he had almost no Adam's apple; and his voice was high-pitched like a woman's. He had only a hint of hair under his arms and none on his chest or belly, and pitifully to kid himself that he was a man, he shaved about once in ten weeks. There were large circles under his eyes, and his private parts were somewhat smaller in size than those of a four-year-old boy. His penis, which the doctors measured, was one inch long and less than half an inch in diameter. He had no testicles that could be detected with certainty.

It is remarkable that he was engaged to be married. He was what's technically called a pre-puberal castrate or eunuchoid.

The chemical fire of his life burned low; his basal metabolic rate was minus seventeen to nineteen; he was full of worries and emotionally gusty, and you can imagine how it would make him feel to be without clothes before other men. On the idea that his lack of genital development might be due to something wrong with the pituitary gland which governs these genital organs, years before he had been given months of injections with a pituitary-like impure hormone that is got out of the urine of pregnant females. Nothing doing.

At this moment in 1937 the pure male hormone was just beginning to come out of the chemists' kettles in the form of testosterone acetate, price prohibitive; and now the chemical firm of Ciba sent James B. Hamilton—for purely scientific purposes—a supply of testosterone that was still worth more than its weight in gold.

For the first time into any American man, so far as published records go, anatomist Hamilton and the doctors sent shots of testosterone into the flabby muscles of this twenty-seven-year-old boy's arm and into those of his buttocks three times a week. Throughout his life he'd experienced only the feeblest and most fleeting sexual sensations; and he was certainly unfair to that girl to have become engaged. Now, within sixty hours of the first injection he began to have erections; after six days this turgor of his penis became more frequent and stronger; the size of his penis at rest became greater; and before the month of testosterone injections was completed, this man, impotent for life, was able to carry on sexual intercourse.

What interested anatomist Hamilton was that testosterone's effect reached far beyond the merely sexual. The boy's thyroid gland began to grow; his larynx became congested, and the doctors thought they could detect a lower pitch to his voice. The hot flashes that had bothered him for years disappeared completely. During that month he had only one attack of the migraine headache that had tortured him so long and so often. A curious new sap of self-confidence flowed through him, and energy, and he looked people in the face and was happy. Hair began to grow on his upper lip and his chest; and when he looked toward tomorrow, he no longer despaired.

Then Hamilton and his doctors played a shrewd scientific trick on their historic human experimental animal. Despite this definitely bigger thyroid gland, his new prostate gland where he'd practically not had one at all before, the hair on his chest and his swelling genitals, even so the experimenters distrusted their own eyes and feared even more that the boy was being fooled by his own imagination. After all, he was a medical student; he knew precisely what Hamilton and the doctors were trying to do to him; after all remarkable cures have been made with sugar pills or injections of salt water; all this manhood might be only a phony. . . . Shades of poor old Brown-Séquard!

So the testosterone injections were stopped, though the boy did not know it. The doctors kept up their injections, but not of testosterone. They were blanks, simply shots of inert oil. In five days he had four hot flashes and then an attack of migraine. The erections of his penis, signals of his new miraculous manhood, began to weaken. His sweetheart did not excite him; and though he fought for them, he was less and less able to stir his feelings. With his new manhood ebbing, at the same time away went his new pride and confidence, and now he was tired all the time again, after doing nothing.

Again, without his knowing it, the experimenters began giving him testosterone, in larger doses this time and in the more powerful form of testosterone propionate, and within a few days there was a startling upsurge in his total vitality and his march toward belated manhood.

Hard-boiled medical skeptics might criticize Hamilton for publishing (as he now proceeded to do) what's sarcastically called "a series of one case," and nothing is more certain in science than that it takes more than one swallow to make a summer. But just the same, there seemed no question that this unfortunate boy was more energetic, virile, and self-assured while on this new testosterone. It wasn't the lad's imagination. His fellow students, not knowing about the experiment, noticed this increase in masculine spunkiness, its disappearance, and its curious return.

"The increase in these qualities was vouchsafed by his associates," wrote Doctor Hamilton primly in his professorial patois.

"Finally," wrote Hamilton in his scientific report, "it

should be noted that no deleterious effects were observed on the blood or urine constituents of the patient."

Did this mean that unhappy eunuchoids (and there are plenty of them, more than you think) can get a new lease on life and live their lives on a borrowed manhood? It was clear that testosterone wouldn't *cure* the tragic defect of these eunuchoid almost-men. It wouldn't create the testicles they'd lacked from the time they were in their mother's womb. To maintain this chemical manhood they'd have to go on and on taking testosterone, probably, the way a severe diabetic keeps himself strong and saves himself from death by life-long injections of insulin.

Hamilton published his little one-cylinder miracle with professorial caution. "The period of treatment of this patient has been short," he wrote. "Further observation and many additional cases must be investigated before generalizations can be made."

His first confirmation came that very same year from Bristol, England, and this new experiment had in it an element of the accidental, since the testosterone was not used primarily on the theory that it might restore a lost manhood. Doctor George L. Foss, of Bristol, England, gave it to a broken man for another purpose; and if there were any effect on the manhood, well, that would be velvet. But Foss mentioned nothing about this to the patient. This was a thirty-eight-year-old veteran of World War I, who complained to Doctor Foss of a nasty eruption on his face and nose, and swollen eyelids and conjunctivitis.

This English war veteran, observed Doctor Foss, was a very strange-looking man for his age. His face looked too smooth and much more as if he were in his twenties. It was as if something had happened to him, bang, and chopped his physical development off short after strong manhood had started. That was exactly what had happened. At Givenchy in France in 1918 when this veteran was only nineteen, a shell-burst had, in fact, robbed him of all chance of completing his mature manly development by smashing up both of his testicles so that they had to be removed entirely. With that wonderful impersonal cruelty inherent in the human institution of war, that high explosive accident had left the boy's penis absolutely unharmed; and now today Doctor Foss, examining him, noted that it was large and well-developed, though useless.

The veteran was now making his living as a foreman electrician. His body was soft; it was as if he had almost no muscles at all; his hips had grown wider and his shoulders seemed narrower than when he was a soldier. He had very little drive. Before his castration in battle, at Givenchy, he told Doctor Foss that the sap of life had run strong in him. He remembered he'd had plenty of libido, only he didn't call it that, but said he wanted a girl, and plenty. He remembered he had been very strong sexually. But now for many years this memory had been fading and fading.

Just the same this veteran had married, in 1924, and you'd wonder why, because the doctors had told him he would surely be impotent. In his honeymoon days he had been able to work up what was not more than a shadow of his pre-war sexual drive. He confessed that he made some attempts at sexual intercourse "for his wife's satisfaction" but he confessed that he had been unable to satisfy her at all.

Curiously, this wasn't what bothered our veteran. He came for that unsightly eruption. After all, when a man's testicles are off, they're off, and nature mercifully, maybe, made him forget how wonderful it had been when he still had them. This is observed by many physicians, questioning castrates. Their loss loses its first poignant tragedy.

Now Doctor Foss had a hunch about treating our veteran's skin disease. There's an eruption exactly like this that's observed in some women at the time of their change of life, coming and going from month to month, cyclic. This can be treated by giving women the female hormone, estradiol.

Now here in 1937 there was the first scientific news of this new pure *male* hormone, testosterone, the male counterpart of the female hormone, so maybe it would have the same effect on our veteran's skin disease. After all, he too was a victim in his own way of what you could call a change of life though slightly more rugged than that of ladies in their forties. Doctor Foss made inquiries, and yes, the firm of Schering would be glad to furnish him a liberal supply of testosterone propionate—for scientific purposes. At this time, the human use for it had not yet been discovered.

Doctor Foss began injecting it into the feeble muscles of this castrated man in good stiff doses.

Within six days the eruption on his skin had cleared. On the eighth day of the injections he came to Doctor Foss as usual and surprised him by asking, pleading, "Doctor, can't you lay off these shots for a while?"

Doctor Foss was puzzled. Wasn't our veteran pleased about the way in which these shots were clearing up his eruption?

Then our veteran, with some shame, confessed that he hadn't slept at all the night before. He had been impotent, as good as sexless, for nineteen years. But last night he had suffered a terrific erection of his penis. For the first time in their married life he could now satisfy his wife. But here was what was terrible. In this strange belated honeymoon, thirteen years after their marriage, nothing could calm our veteran's terrific sexual turgor. It was awfully painful. It is that state of untameable erection the doctors call "priapism."

Doctor Foss was excited by the result of his experiment. "To obviate any effect of suggestion I had not questioned him previously about the influence of the injections on his sexual function, and he thought these were being given only for his skin condition," reported the good doctor.

Now the veteran told him that *ever since the very first in-*

jection, erection had been more ready and that he had coitus every night. After the fifth injection, erections were rapid and prolonged; and what made his wife so contented failed to relieve him.

So Doctor Foss now cut down the number of testosterone injections to twice a week. That was the wonderful thing about this crystal pure male hormone—you could dose it precisely. The pain went out of our veteran's sexual excitement, but his new sex drive remained. And shortly, and with happiness, our veteran reported to Doctor Foss that he was sexually strong and normal, just as he'd been before Givenchy, when he was only nineteen. For thirteen years his wife had never obtained any satisfaction, but now his return to sexual power had enabled him to satisfy her completely.

But that wasn't all. During twelve weeks of treatment he had gained eighteen pounds, and all his clothes had become too small. Originally, he wore fourteen-and-a-half-inch collars. Now fifteen-and-a-half were too tight. Unlike many castrates and eunuchs, our veteran had not been morbid or depressed by his condition; yet Doctor Foss had to admit that now there was a soaring in his general physical and mental condition. He was proud to be a man again.

It seemed as if Fred Koch's prophecy were coming true. While he was groping for the chemical structure of the male hormone among those tons of bull's testicles in the late nineteen twenties and early thirties he had said: "The exact chemical nature of the product should be known; it should be pure; its physiological activity should be accurately assayed on mammals."

Now testosterone, of which Koch had been the forerunner, satisfied these stern requirements, better than insulin, better than any hormone from the all-powerful pituitary, as well as any hormone yet discovered.

In his Chicago laboratory Koch was modestly pleased and proud of the triumph of the European chemists, of Butenandt and Ružička and Laqueur's men, that had resulted from Koch's own trail-blazing.

In his quiet way Koch had been the Moses and now he was living to see the Promised Land. "With these pure products available," he wrote, "we should now be able to solve more definitely and more rapidly the numerous biological and clinical problems in this complex endocrine field."

What Koch really meant was that this complex endocrine field, at least the male hormone corner of it, was now going to be more simple. When doctors had to work with a variable chemical gunk like the extracts of the pituitary, they never knew exactly what they were injecting. Now testosterone, pure, was like a key to a lock. It either fitted the lock or it didn't. It either satisfied a suspected hormone hunger or it failed to. You could get your answer, not maybe, but yes or no.

And in the cases of the Albany medical student and the Bristol war veteran the answers to testosterone had been a clear-cut yes.

In Albany, testosterone had made a man of a boy who before could have had no chance to be manly. In Bristol, testosterone had resurrected a broken man to a manhood he had lost forever.

CHAPTER FIFTEEN

PONDERING the history of the male hormone I pinched myself to see if I was awake or only dreaming. It seemed too clear-cut and simple. Could it be that testosterone was going to be found to be the master key to unlock waning total vitality in men? These pre-puberty and post-puberty eunuchoids were exactly the human experimental animals that you needed to test it, precisely like laboratory castrated white rats or capons. The experimental human material was yelling to be tested. There were plenty of God-forgotten men who'd been bereft of their sex glands by war wounds, by industrial accidents, by mumps, tuberculosis, and other diseases. Now that the news of testosterone was getting about by these first publications and by the scientific grapevine, the doctors would certainly begin rounding up these unfortunates.

They were unfortunate and not only sexually. To these forlorn ones the loss of sex-drive is a minor tragedy in a half-life to which death itself would be preferable. Their muscles fag when their day's work is just beginning; their skin grows gray and fails to color to the wind and the sun; they try to think, and they are foiled by an aimless woolgathering; their hope for tomorrow fades into despond, unrelieved by frequent tears or sullen anger.

Such are the post-puberty accidentally castrated eunuchoids; and the fate of the almost-men, "born eunuchs from their mother's womb," is just as sad and as serious. These cases of arrested sexual development are more numerous than we know, since their pitiful condition is hidden. The sexual organs of these hypogonads, as they're called in hormone hunter's jargon, remain infantile; they have thin fair skin and high-pitched voices; they lack hair on their faces and bodies; their muscles are small and feminine, and their lives are frustrated by much the same physical and mental tiredness that afflicts the broken men.

Could it actually be that testosterone would stoke up the total vitality in the great majority of these almost-men who had never felt high total vitality at all? Could it actually be that the new pure male hormone would resurrect the total vitality of the broken men who'd lost it for years?

Nothing is more common or more tragic than the dashing of hopes raised by new remedies; these new medical brooms almost always sweep too clean. That's why doctors have a perfect right to their skepticism about any new serum, hormone, or chemical—till its value is tested in the white hot fire of the clinic by men who are honest and disillusioned. Now remembering these two miracles, the one at Albany and the other at Bristol, England, I looked myself in the face and admitted that for me they were not enough. For me they were nothing. All my life I had been thumbing my nose at medical authority and looking for discoveries not by medical pooh-bahs but by medical guerillas, and yet, and yet, even for me there was nothing so comforting and cozy about a medical discovery as to have it confirmed at a great and conservative university.

Disrespectful myself, I really only believed a discovery when it became academically reputable. At heart I had to admit I was a scientific bourgeois, about as bad as the most stuffy professor. Now regarding the seeming new magic of testosterone, I grievously wanted the comfort of its approbation by a man whom I scientifically trusted, to whom I looked up as to a father. And now at this moment a scientific publication caught my eye. It was about testosterone. It was from the medical holy of holies, from the Johns Hopkins University. Its authors were the excellent investigators, Samuel A. Vest, Jr., and John Eager Howard. It was a passage on page 157 of their paper that excited me.

"Young and one of us (1937) suggested the possible value of testosterone in cases of hypogonadism, and presented a preliminary report. . . . The results obtained at that time indicated what might be expected from the use of testosterone in the human," wrote Doctors Vest and Howard.

Young? That meant Doctor Hugh Hampton Young. This meant that the famous Hugh Young was fathering testosterone pioneering which had begun so obscurely in Albany, New York, and Bristol, England. In his own field Hugh Young (though he'd made his scientific mistakes like any other human) was to me like Herman Bundesen and Jacques Loeb and Charles F. Kettering. Like them Hugh Young was disillusioned yet invincibly optimistic. If Hugh Young was now sponsoring this trial of testosterone, then it must at least be something.

Hugh Young has won his place among the surgical immortals. He is tall and keen-eyed and soldierly and wonderfully shrewd yet candid. He is human. He admits he has wept because his science was still powerless to save a dear friend's life from cancer. He roars with laughter, hiding whiskey bottles from a snooping bishop who was out to expose the boozing of high officers of the A.E.F. in World War I.

Young is a complex man. He is a urologic surgeon whose fame and income throughout a large part of his life stemmed in part from the prevalence of gonorrhea that's a reward of sexual sin. At the same time, during the first World War, he had been boss of the then most brilliant campaign on record to prove the possibility of wiping out this same sickness—on which much of his livelihood depended.

It was in Hugh Young's clinic that the power of the first of the sulfa drugs really to *cure* gonorrhea was demonstrated.

Hugh Young is a surgeon so bold, ingenious and patiently

pernickety that his prostate operation first demonstrated the possibility of reducing deaths from such prostatectomies down close to zero. He is that kind of fighter for life. Yet he's a soldier. During World War I he tried to finagle himself out of the medical corps to get into the infantry to become a killer.

Hugh Young is the first citizen of Baltimore, grave in Prince Albert, striped pants, and with a gold-headed cane. That hasn't prevented him from being a kind of village cut-up, a concocter of obscene medical buffooneries. He is in his way an artist, physicist, engineer, plumber, and profound surgical biologist. Yet he can frivol away his precious time, risking his life as he did some years ago to fly in an old crate of a French mail plane two thousand miles in the wind and rain for a peep into the harem of the Grand Pasha of Marrakech.

Hugh Young is conservative in the tradition of the snootiest Baltimore blue bloods, setting the town by the ears to arrange a swank luncheon for aristocratic Anthony Eden. At the same time he's a radical, fighting for laws against tuberculosis that will mean life to Maryland's poor white people and colored children.

Hugh Young's operating rooms have been battle grounds for forty-five years. He is a super-plumber of human drainpipes, those of all conditions of men from Presidents to paupers. He pays due respect to chastity and with gay cynicism —not unhealthy!—he hints that the roots of sexual virtue lie in impotence. Here is the man really to give a fair trial to testosterone.

Hugh Young is very American, in the best pioneer tradition, because he is hardly ever gloomy and tragic and always hopeful. He will not be stopped by the male hormone's sexiness. As a great public healthman, which he is over and above his urologic discipline, he is a-moral, objective. He showed that in World War I in the scandal of St. Nazaire.

At the human sink of iniquity that St. Nazaire was then, turned as it was into a mass-production Sodom and Gomorrah by our doughboys who were young human animals before they were heroes, Hugh Young looked with awe that was not so much horrified as it was enthusiastic. Here was human lechery on a belt line. Here was syphilis, not rampant, but well-nigh ubiquitous. Here was mass fornication that would have left old Doctor François Rabelais stuttering to find adjectives.

At the dismayed orders of General Pershing, Hugh Young went to St. Nazaire, gazed into its human sump pit, deplored it—but perfunctorily—and then proceeded to bring against it the power of modern science, unchained absolutely. He brushed aside the French medical incompetents, that medical man Clémenceau, himself, included, who believed that you could control venereal diseases by merely inspecting those rouged Magdalens who spread them. He declared those bad girls out of bounds; and when the venereal battle's smoke cleared away, it was Hugh Young who was thanked for a drop by five-sixths in prevalence of new venereal infections in our army.

He was certainly the man to father testosterone research, with all its disreputable implications because down deep in his heart he did not take himself too seriously. Candidly he tells the story of his first contact with the God, Bacchus, that he has worshipped all his life. When he was a toddler of eighteen months, he stole a whiskey bottle from his father and mother, while they were disrobing after a hard day's journey. He tossed off its contents, got roaring drunk, and all that night made merry. A man with that kind of candor about himself will surely not be hypocritical about certain strange powers that might be possessed by this new male hormone.

There was another reason for my faith in Hugh Young. He had saved the lives of two of my best friends by his surgical wizardry when both of these men had been given up for dead. But there was a final and ultimate reason for my new confidence, finding this maestro among the very first medical men examining into the power of testosterone. It's to be found in his diary, written on his seventieth birthday.

"Up at 6:30. Usual exercises; excellent coördinated movement. Cold shower. Light breakfast. Dash to hospital. Began operating 8:15. Interesting cases: one from Cuba, the other from Haiti. Operative notes dictated while dressing and coming down the elevator. By motor for fishing grounds with Warren; on Belvedere shoals at 1:00 P.M.; fine afternoon's fishing. Dinner at home. By motor to Washington to sign important papers. To bed at midnight. Prayer: Thanks, dear God, for manifold blessings vouchsafed me during my first seventy years. Please make the second seventy more fruitful."

Here is a man who himself does not need testosterone. But here is a man, like Herman Bundesen, who looks into the future. So now I devoured the description of the experiments with the new male hormone by Hugh Young's disciples, John Eager Howard and Samuel A. Vest, Jr.

There was a touch of Hugh Young's own bold originality in their account of testosterone's strange power over the life of one of the first human beings upon whom they tried it, in 1937. This was a little Negro boy only three and a half years old. He had extensive tumors in his larynx so that he could hardly breathe, so that a tracheal tube had to be inserted. But why should they give him testosterone? They gave it because such larynx tumors, though resistant to treatment in young children, tend to vanish spontaneously at the time of puberty. This is the time when the natural male hormone becomes active in the human body. So there was a chance that the new synthetic hormone, testosterone, might cure these growths in the little Negro boy's throat.

Now Doctors Vest and Howard began injecting this colored boy with testosterone, cautiously, with small doses of twenty milligrams of testosterone benzoate, once a week. They observed the boy for five months and there was no effect, alas, on the larynx tumors at all. But the transformation of the little Negro boy was terrific.

Within that five months he developed pubic hair, and grotesquely, what was practically a man's sized penis. His muscles developed remarkably. He showed unusual strength for his size. Like a little gorilla, he climbed in and out of his crib, the kind that easily imprisoned the other children. He had been a nice gentle little boy, but now he became belligerent. He battled all the other children all over the ward and completely overpowered them. He was a holy terror. Testosterone, given to him in small doses for a year, jumped him many years ahead of his natural development toward an eerie, premature manhood.

But when the injections were stopped, there having been no curative effect on the throat tumors, gradually this precocious manhood vanished. His premature sexual excitement ebbed. He stopped being a bully. Curiously he became thoughtful, gentle, and almost mother-like in his relations with other children.

Yes, manhood is chemical, manhood is testosterone; and now the Johns Hopkins doctors reported its miraculous effect upon twenty-two men devoid of sexual power. These were almost-men who had never had any manhood and broken men who'd been robbed of manhood by accidents or disease. Like a chemical key in a chemical lock, testosterone opened the door of new life to all of them. They all became as normal men, sexually. They felt their surge of sex drive as early as the second day after the injections started. As the treatment continued, hair grew abundantly on their bodies. And among those inborn eunuchoids who had been so ashamed of their childish voices, speech now quickly deepened to that of mature manhood. Those who were thin, gained from ten to twenty-five pounds in weight.

The power of testosterone was beyond the merely sexual. Many of these almost-men and broken men showed a new surge of general strength and energy; and there was a rapid increase in the muscular development of several of them. One of them who had been especially shy, bashful, and hating to associate with men of his own age, changed remarkably. He became self-confident and optimistic. All of these forlorn and formerly feeble fellows became more aggressive and quicker on the trigger and more capable in their daily work. In every instance there was extraordinary improvement in their spirits, in what the doctors called their psychological outlook. They were hopeful now, and cheerful.

The power of testosterone was more than a flash in the pan. These twenty-two men were continued under the treatment for two years, and there was no waning of their new manhood, and all of them clamored to keep on taking these life-giving injections.

There seemed no doubt that testosterone was the complete answer to a lack of the male hormone that's the internal secretion of the human testicles.

Nobody could object to this magic new life for the almost-men and the resurrection of those castrates whose lives had been broken. But, looked at in the broadest moral sense, when this new testosterone got into real chemical mass production (it was still rare and expensive) wouldn't it then be dangerous, be dynamite to turn loose on humanity? After all these forlorn eunuchoids had a right to normal life, and they were no great part of humanity, in numbers. But what about testosterone's possible effect upon our young men who were already too, too sexual and wanted to be still more so? It was a disturbing question for clergymen, social workers, and all upright and serious citizens.

A reassuring answer came from Doctors Vest and Howard. They had put this to strict experiment. They had got volunteers among "normal" husky young fellows and had given them double-sized injections of testosterone; and upon none of these "normal" young men had there been any sexual effect at all.

This seemed clear: it's only when you lack natural male hormone that testosterone shows its magic power, and it can't make you any more manly than manly. And what's more, the new male hormone seemed unable to relieve the sexual impotence of men whose sexual apparatus *seemed* normal. Together with the distinguished psychiatrist, Doctor Thomas A. C. Rennie, our Johns Hopkins physicians tried out testosterone upon eight men who had full development of their testicles and other signs of manhood. They were what is called psychically impotent. These unfortunates were not in the slightest degree set afire by the powerful male hormone.

The Johns Hopkins physicians pointed out the complexity of the human male as a sexual machine. Without testicles, in general this sexual machinery fails to function. Yet there are exceptions even here, as in certain rare cases of castrated men who are still able to have erections. But there are other mysterious influences besides testosterone that seem able to stoke up sex fire or to dampen it. Over and beyond testosterone, manhood seems to be partly a state of mind.

Doctors Vest and Howard proved this amusingly upon a man working in their clinic. This fellow was fifty-five years old. He was a technician who'd worked most of his life among doctors, an observant, intelligent man; and he was excited by the miracles performed by testosterone upon the impotence of the almost-men and those broken men who'd been robbed of their sex glands. He still enjoyed the thrill of romance and felt that his own sexual powers could stand a bit of reconditioning. Upon being questioned closely, he admitted that, whereas in the old days he had been able to perform sexual intercourse three times of an evening, now one time was as much as he could manage, and this irked his pride.

He was at this time contemplating a romantic evening;

and now he begged the doctors for an injection of this new elixir that so transformed those sexless men. Doctors Vest and Howard obliged him, in the interests of science, and gave him a shot of twice the ordinary dose; they gave him fifty milligrams of testosterone propionate. For the technician the experiment seemed a great success. Next morning he came walking in as if on air and said that he had been able to perform the sexual rite three times, as of yore.

The physicians were pretty sure that this remarkable result had been pure suggestion, a result of the man's imagination. So, when that technician came to them a month later, asking for another injection, again in the interests of science, the doctors made a new experiment. They took two little vials, containing no testosterone at all, nothing but sterile oil. They labeled them "testosterone propionate—twenty-five milligrams." They took good care that the technician saw those labels when they prepared the injection.

Once more (for the technician) the experiment was a brilliant success; and the injections, though completely blank, produced exactly the same effect as the first shot of real testosterone. The doctors, to make scientifically sure, played their little scientific trick upon the trusting fellow again and again; and each time he reported that these wonderful shots made him every bit of the man he used to be. Their mighty power really disturbed him, seeming to extend beyond his nights of love.

Even the next day, so he said, he remained so excited sexually that it interfered with his work at the clinic.

Studying these careful scientific reports of the Johns Hopkins doctors, it was plain to me that they believed that testosterone's action, though marvelous, was sharply limited. It could fantastically speed up the strength and sexual development of a three-and-a-half-year-old boy. It could make men of human beings who'd remained tragically boyish far beyond the ordinary time of puberty. It could resurrect men who had been broken by castration, by disease, or by accident, so that a new sap flowed through their feeble and flabby muscles; so that their gray skin that had failed to tan to sunshine, now began to bronze; so that their thoughts ran strong and uninterrupted by their old self-pity; so that they were actually transformed from prematurely aged men to energetic, cheerful, social beings.

But that was all; that seemed to be the end of it. These experiments, brilliant though they were, held no promise for the army of millions of men whose total vitality slowly drained away as they moved through life's afternoon toward its twilight.

Could it be that observers, ancient and modern, were mistaken in believing that the total vitality of men and animals is tied up to their sexual vigor?

Could it be true, as Vest and Howard seemed to think, that testosterone only held promise for eunuchoid men who had been born without testicles or who, after puberty, had been robbed of them?

Was the slow waning of total vitality in normal men (who did have sex glands) due to other causes than a mere lack of testosterone?

Was Herman Bundesen putting the cart before the horse? Could it be, in normal men who did have testicles, that the ability of these glands to produce male hormone depended upon their total vitality, rather than the total vitality depending on the testosterone?

Was it an entirely false theory that older, normal men, losing the vigor and fire of their youth gradually, might be suffering a slow chemical castration that took place invisibly with the passage of time?

At this point in my gloomy doubts I brought myself up short. "Wait a bit," I told myself, "don't be too damned respectful of high medical authority." It was very comforting to find the first proof of a limited power of testosterone confirmed at one of the greatest medical institutions in the world, at the Johns Hopkins University. And yet, even if the Johns Hopkins doctors had given me confidence in what testosterone could do, I shouldn't be too quickly swept off my feet by their assertions of what it *couldn't* do. Careful and brilliant as their experiments were, even so, in this vast unknown field, they had hardly so much as scratched the surface. Many a promising extension of knowledge has been killed in its cradle by a man of high scientific authority saying with a contemptuous smile, "Zilch of Johns Hopkins or Harvard or Yale or Michigan says there's nothing to it."

Among many men of medical science there is a curious dark joy in smearing a hopeful scientific advance, assassinating it without trying it or without trying it thoroughly and impartially.

Now I looked back carefully into the excellent scientific report of Doctors Vest and Howard, and detected a hint of prejudice against testosterone's having an effect upon normal men with testicles. It appeared in the famous case of that fifty-five-year-old technician who'd been rejuvenated by those blank injections.

Here's what Doctors Howard and Vest wrote: "Believing his medication to have been effective solely through suggestion. . . ." That was the devil of it. *Believing* before they made the experiment. They had a preconceived idea that testosterone would have an effect only on men without testicles. And so, when that blank injection gave the testosterone effect on just one man with testicles, they called it a day. They'd confirmed their prejudice. By a series of just one case. What if they'd been truly scientific about it? What if they'd set up an experiment upon a hundred fifty-five-year-old men with testicles, the men not knowing what they were getting, half of them getting blanks and half of them real testosterone? And then reporting, yes or no, whether there was a surge in their general or sexual vigor. That would have been science.

On this technician all they'd proved is that there can be a great power of suggestion regarding sexual potency. In one man.

Then, too, there was that other test the Johns Hopkins doctors had made together with the psychiatrist, Doctor Thomas A. C. Rennie. Testosterone had failed to stoke up sexual fire in eight men who were psychically impotent. This series of eight cases was nothing. The next eight impotent men they tried with testosterone might have been set to prancing like so many stallions. How much impotence is psychic and how much a testosterone deficiency, and what does that word "psychic" really mean? After all, as old Voltaire said, the psyche, the soul is something about which the priests know a great deal and the physicians next to nothing. Scientifically, in such a dark unknown field as this one, a series of eight cases is almost as bad as a series of one.

What if they had taken hundreds of "psychically" impotent men of all ages, but with testicles (the woods are full of them) and what if they'd given half of them blanks and half of them testosterone, the men not knowing? That would be science.

Now I pulled myself up short and tried to gather my wits and set my common sense to working. I began asking myself positive instead of negative questions.

If testosterone brought back muscular strength, mental keenness, joy in life to broken men without testicles, bringing them back to normal, wasn't it likely that this same testosterone did play a role in keeping up the muscle and brain power of normal men?

Wasn't it natural for the activity of the testicles to wane with age?

What was so cockeyed about supposing that injections of testosterone might replace what the aging testicles were no longer so active in producing?

It seemed altogether too simple to say that testosterone

could help only those men who had no testicles that the doctor could see or could feel. And just because a testicle did exist so that the physician could see it or feel it, that didn't mean that it was working. For example, a man may have what looks like a healthy pancreas, yet be dying of diabetes because that pancreas doesn't produce insulin.

Now I looked at the immense bibliography of scientific reports on testosterone that lay before me. Here was a report by the excellent medical observer, Doctor E. Perry McCullagh, of Cleveland, Ohio. It seemed, according to Doctor McCullagh, that sex gland deficiency didn't necessarily have to be visible, it could be functional. Here was McCullagh's report of a fifty-eight-year-old man. It's true that his testicles were rather small, but he had them just the same. He was irritable, excitable, melancholic, and almost completely impotent. Within two weeks after testosterone treatment began, he was sexually normal and calm and almost completely out of his mental depression.

This again was only a series of one case, admitted. But before me lay a bibiography of almost one thousand scientific reports on testosterone that had come from hospitals and laboratories all over the world in the seven short years since Leopold Ružička had begun making the pure synthetic male hormone in Zurich, Switzerland. Glancing through these titles, it was clear that by no means the majority of these reports dealt with the use of testosterone merely upon men who had no sex glands. And it seemed possible, beginning the study of these publications, that testosterone might have life-building powers far beyond the sexual.

CHAPTER SIXTEEN

DIGGING into the history of a possible broader use of testosterone than its mere rescue of eunuchoids, I determined not to confine myself too closely to reports from the great medical schools on our eastern seaboard. In trying to find out testosterone's tie-up to male human vitality, it seemed wise to take what might be called geographical psychology into consideration. Much of our American medical science had been cradled in Harvard, Cornell, Columbia, and the Johns Hopkins Universities; but these days they're not making, by a long shot, all the discoveries; and at the same time there is a tendency of their medical nabobs to be snooty to searchers west of the Alleghanies and to regard them as medical aborigines. Now, in a field so new, so morally disturbing, so fantastic in its possibilities as that of testosterone, why not take a look westward? Out there the medical boys, though possibly lacking the eastern cultural medical profundity, might tend to be a bit bolder and open-minded in their experiments—not quite so stuffy.

This brought me to study the work of a urologic surgeon, Doctor Walter M. Kearns, of Milwaukee, Wisconsin. There was obvious accuracy and at the same time a forward-thrusting sweep to his testing of both the male and the female sex hormones. Nationally, as a urologist Doctor Kearns commands respect, belonging to the American Urologic Association which is the highest-brow organization of these indispensable plumbers of the human body. Stirred by the stories told in his clearly-written papers on the hormones, both male and female, I got to know Walter Kearns personally.

Big, genial but tough, radiating technical competence, Kearns is the type of surgeon you'd not hesitate (especially when you're suspicious of all knives) to trust with your own life. I had confidence in him especially because he belongs to that superb new modern breed of knife-men who are on a constant hunt for science that will make this or that profitable operation no longer necessary. It was clear that Kearns was demonstrating the chemical power of sex hormones over the machinery of that part of the human anatomy of which he himself was a master mechanic. He was observing this or that hormone control over urological diseases. That would certainly knock out part of his surgical practice. He's the kind of man that you trust.

Walter Kearns was especially excited by a strange power of the sex hormones that is biologically deepest, strangest, altogether most fundamental. This was the uncanny ability of one of the pure female hormones to alter the lives and the fate of men, and of the pure male hormone—testosterone—to bring about deep changes in the sex lives of women. This had gripped Kearns and had led him into what looked like a hopeful, life-saving experimentation upon certain men who seemed absolutely doomed to die.

This curious antagonism, this chemical war between the male and female hormones, seemed a chemical miniature of the well-known human war between men and women. Take the male hormone, testosterone. It can repress the menstruation of girls entering puberty; it can inhibit menstruation in women and can bring on their change of life; it can stop milk secretion in the breasts of nursing mothers. Take one of the female hormones, the one called estradiol. Large doses of estradiol have wiped sexual desire clean out of a sexual criminal, have made him meek as a lambkin, have knocked out the ability of his testicles to form sperm, have brought about actual degeneration of the sperm-forming cells of his sex glands.

To Kearns, the chemical hair-line that separates men from women was fantastic. Testosterone and estradiol are the closest kind of chemical brothers and sisters in the organic chemical family called steroids. They're both built out of exactly the same hexagon and pentagon arrangement of seventeen carbon and twenty-eight hydrogen atoms that goes by the organic chemical name of cyclo pentano perhydro phenanthrene—only the organic chemists run all those words together. Chemically all of us are both man and woman because our bodies make both male and female hormone, and, primarily, it's an excess of testosterone that makes us men or an excess of female hormones that makes us women; and the chemical difference between testosterone and estradiol is merely a matter of four atoms of hydrogen and one atom of carbon.

This should give all novelists, poets, and moralists pause; it should really give all of us the shivers.

Kearns explained to me how the relative amounts—in the bodies of men—of testosterone and estradiol may actually mean the difference between life and death. The very presence of the prostate gland in men depends upon testosterone; and one of the deadliest cancers in men is that of the prostate, killing more men over forty than any other kind of cancer excepting that of the stomach. Here testosterone, said Kearns, far from strength-giving, is a chemical accessory to the crime.

This had been proved by the University of Chicago searcher, Charles Scott Huggins, who had discovered that when you castrate far-gone victims of prostate cancer, and so remove their primary source of testosterone, the terrible pain of their cancer fades. And in many of them, the cancer cells that have spread to their bones, lungs, or livers stop growing. Without testosterone, these wild prostate cells lose their deadly anarchy and often begin to wither away.

Testosterone doesn't cause cancer in men, but it is an important factor in the continued growth of cancer cells in any part of the body, provided the cancer originated in the prostate gland. For the cancer cells are wild children of the normal cells of the prostate, whose growth is dominated by the male hormone.

It is certainly tough and drastic to have to deprive a man of his testicles; but in cancer of the prostate, it was at least a straw of hope if you wanted to live. Heretofore, when cancer of the prostate was diagnosed, the surgical removal of the prostate gland was futile in all but a small percentage of cases. The cancer had already escaped to other parts of the body.

At the time I met him, Walter Kearns was in the excitement of what looked very much like life-saving experiments against this deadly disease, by an actual chemical control that would make the castration needless. If testosterone is the chemical villain in prostate cancer, then why not scotch it by giving the doomed victims the opposite, the female hormone? Other searchers had had some preliminary success with the hormone-like chemical, stilbestrol. But now Kearns was testing what he called "the old ladies' hormone"—ethinyl estradiol. It was twenty times stronger than stilbestrol in its action.

So now he was excited about some fifty men who had been doomed to die of cancer of the prostate. They belonged to that sad cohort of thousands of men who drag out a life of a few months to a few years, tortured with pain, relieved only by loading them with opiates, gradually deteriorating to an existence from which death relieves them, mercifully. Here now were more than two-thirds of that group of fifty. The day after their first shot of ethinyl estradiol, the frightful pain in their bones and other parts of their cancerous bodies had left them. Their wild cancer cells were tamed, so long as they kept on taking little doses of ethinyl estradiol. They were not bed-ridden. They were walking about and working. They were miraculously well and living. They had come back from the grave. It was too soon to say they were cured. But they had a new lease on life. Many were alive and well for five years since their doom had been diagnosed. They were chemically guarded from torture and death by the old ladies' hormone *that antagonized their own male hormone*, testosterone.

It was plain that Kearns, who knew the grim two-edged power of testosterone, would not be the kind of man who'd regard it as a universal elixir. At this time testosterone was already being very widely used to relieve the urinary troubles of middle-aged men with simple enlargement of the prostate gland. And here Walter Kearns said doctors should certainly step mighty carefully. A simple enlargement of the prostate gland might hide an early prostate cancer. And giving testosterone in such cases would surely light up the cancer fire—in fact, Kearns had seen two men in which this had actually happened. If any doctor was going to give testosterone for simple prostate trouble, it was his absolute duty first to rule out prostate cancer, said Kearns.

Yet from a wide experience with testosterone that he'd given to men young, middle-aged, and old, to eunuchoid men and to normal men with testicles, he was sure that the male hormone was fundamental—in all manner of men—to their total vitality.

Like the Johns Hopkins doctors, Kearns had begun with castrates. They were patients who had made the rounds of several physicians, he said, and they'd got the usual futile ministrations with preparation injected or by mouth, ending in despair. They were broken men—nervous, apprehensive, depressed, unable to concentrate and devoid of desire, with pale, sallow, thin wrinkled skin. They could at best only hold part time positions. Now testosterone transformed them in every way; and Kearns said it was comical how one of these most down-at-heel broken fellows rebelled at this resurrection, yet couldn't get along without it. He was an orderly working in a hospital and extremely religious; and now when these shots of testosterone stoked new great sexual fires in him, he had a conviction of sin. He wanted to stop the testosterone treatment.

But it was wonderful the way he could now work, hard, all day, and not be tired in the evening. He decided that his new sin was the lesser of evils and stuck to the testosterone injections.

What puzzled Kearns was the machinery, the mechanism of this surge of total vitality. He was more of an engineer, really, than a physician; and it wasn't enough to say that testosterone was a tonic; that was the jargon of your old horse-and-buggy doctor. It was too vague to say that it gave these forlorn fellows new pep; that sounded like a radio advertisement for vitamins. Now he teamed up with the skilled physiologist, Doctor Ernst Simonson, and his helper, Doctor Norbert Enzer. The three of them tested these resurrected men the way you'd measure the power of an automobile motor on a dynamometer. They put them on endurance tests before testosterone and after.

There was now a new form of the pure male hormone, methyl testosterone that you could give in the form of simple pills by mouth, far more practical than the old testosterone propionate that had to be given in a doctor's office by injections. Ten of these pills, given daily to these broken men, quickly raised their weight-lifting power by seventy-six per cent, raised their weight-holding power by forty-one per cent; and they recovered thirty per cent faster after tiring. The testosterone pills not only increased their muscular endurance but cut down the *fatigability* of their nervous systems; you could measure that by the way their eyes increased their power to distinguish the flickering of a rapidly flashing light.

But what interested me most deeply was that this magical effect of testosterone upon the vigor of nerves and muscles

wasn't confined to eunuchoid almost-men and broken men.
It wasn't as the Johns Hopkins doctors had led me to believe.
These Milwaukee biological engineers made determinations
of testosterone's action on men with testicles, men from
fifty-three to sixty-seven years old, who'd come simply complaining of various nervous symptoms, of being very, very
tired from very little work; and they were impotent.

While the response to testosterone was far less striking
than it had been in those eunuchoids, yet aging men, too,
showed a definite, measurable improvement in the power of
their nerves and muscles.

Kearns found that you didn't need all this exact dynamo-
metric science and its gadgets to know that testosterone had
transformed these broken and these aging men. Along with
their new hopefulness and the new twinkle in their eyes, you
could feel their new life when they shook hands with you,
their grip was so much stronger, and you could see it the
way they walked faster and with a spring in their step and
the way they could go upstairs without stopping.

Kearns saw that the power of testosterone was far beyond
the merely sexual. The Johns Hopkins doctors, when they'd
tried the male hormone out on normal men, who had testicles,
seem to have been interested mainly in its ability to cure their
sexual impotence. But now, giving testosterone pills to older
men, Kearns found that there were doses of the male hormone measured so that it would boost their muscle and
nerve strength, their endurance and general vitality without
having an effect upon their ability to perform sexual intercourse.

The effect of the pure male hormone on a normal, sexually
competent young man, thirty-seven years old, was curious.
An injection of testosterone did not make him sexually more
so. In fact, its effect was opposite; it definitely lowered his
sex desire and drive. But at the same time his muscular tone
and his endurance went up, definitely.

It was clear that testosterone did not turn a young man into a Don Juan, yet it might have a definite up-surging effect on his total vitality. Kearns agreed with the Johns Hopkins physicians that there was plenty of sexual impotence in younger men (so-called psychic impotence) that testosterone couldn't touch. He warned against the misuse of testosterone now that you could take it in the form of pills, and now that its increasing production was beginning to make it cheaper.

"Testosterone must not be given indiscriminately to every knave who aspired to emulate the behavior of the rooster or the squirrel," said Kearns.

Older men, he said, and he meant men with testicles, so-called normal men, who were impotent, were more apt to be benefited by testosterone. But here again you could clearly tell that testosterone had a general life-building as well as a sexual action. Moderate doses of testosterone wiped the nervousness and tiredness out of many of them. Larger doses brought back their sex drive to some.

I was encouraged by this very human, yet coldly experimenting, Milwaukee surgeon's horse sense about testosterone's possibility of lifting the total vitality of millions of men drifting toward life's late afternoon. Here was Kearns; certainly as a hard-boiled investigator he was the opposite of poor old Brown-Séquard. Nobody could accuse Kearns of fooling himself, or of any intention to set up in practice as Doctor Ponce de Leon. Yet he curiously wasn't afraid to use this terrible word "rejuvenation" that made so many doctors see red.

Kearns put me straight on my puzzlement about the widespread medical fear and suspicion of testosterone.

"What's kept the conservatives of medicine careful guarding testosterone against possibilities of future abuse in rejuvenation," he said, "is the popular misconception that rejuvenation is based entirely upon sex."

Here I thought that he was off the beam just a little.

This misconception is not only popular, it's medical, and shared by many a doctor. Many of them will wink at you roguishly and get set to hear a dirty story when you bring up the subject of testosterone.

Yet here he was on the beam again. Rejuvenation's no dirty word to anybody clearly understanding testosterone's action. "Successful rejuvenation for the aged," Kearns said, "brings about clearer mental processes, better functions of the vital organs, a marked increase in energy and drive and a decided uplift in mental outlook."

Kearns was speaking now for our millions of sensible, wise, older men, the vast majority of men who have the good taste to act their age.

"That rejuvenation *may* bring with it a return of sexual activity is of secondary importance," he said.

Definitely testosterone was not the dynamite that doctors thought it to be originally.

"Possibly," said Walter Kearns, "members of the medical profession have been too reluctant in testing the action of testosterone in the light of accumulating reports giving assurance that with elderly men the prolonged use of relatively large doses of this hormone is harmless."

"Since the side reactions are beneficial rather than injurious, further tests seem justified," he said cautiously.

CHAPTER SEVENTEEN

WHAT the common sense of Walter Kearns did for me, mentally, was to blow the predominating sexuality out of testosterone. He made it chemical. He gave it an immense dignity as a key life chemical alongside those other respectable hormones of the pancreas, thyroid, and adrenal glands. He took the stress off its use merely as a savior of eunuchoid almost-men and broken men. He gave me confidence to think that the woes and troubles and low vital fire of these broken men whose sex glands were gone might also be suffered, though maybe in a less degree, by normal men whose sex glands were under par or were aging. Kearns made me understand what marvelous experimental human animals these broken men really were. Their sickness and their low total vitality, conquered so brilliantly by testosterone, were clues to what might be at the bottom of God knew what sickness and low total vitality among normal men, the cause of which was still mysterious and unknown. After all, it was a mighty experiment that nature had performed on these sad and forlorn human beings. It was absolutely parallel in its scientific method to all the basic discoveries made by hormone hunters upon the other glands of internal secretion. How, indeed, had they discovered the terrific power of the various hormones?

Simply by removing this or that gland from an animal and then finding out what went wrong.

In the case of the human testicles these experiments had been made by God in the case of the almost-men, and by accident or disease among the men who'd been born with sex glands and then lost them. And now here was a marvelous scientific weapon, testosterone, that could be used to test out whether this or that symptom, sickness, woe, trouble, or sign of low total vitality might or might not be due to sex glands that were not healthy, not lusty, not functioning at full capacity, that were, in short, as the hormone hunters said, *deficient*.

In the latter part of the nineteen-thirties the bolder and more imaginative hormone-hunting physicians in Europe and America more and more saw the glowing possibility of this new science; and on many a mysterious sickness, they now began testing out the new male hormone; and on many they failed; and on some they got strange and unsuspected positive answers.

Doctor Charles W. Dunn of Philadelphia was one of the bolder and one of the earliest of these explorers. He was visiting endocrinologist to the Delaware State Hospital, the polite and kinder and more accurate name for an insane asylum. A twenty-eight-year-old man was brought to the notice of Doctor Dunn. His mental troubles were completely mysterious. He had first been admitted to the hospital in 1935, two years before; and since that time he had been in and out of several institutions. He was a drunk. And when the doctors examined him at this present admission they put their physical examination down as essentially negative—except for a hangover.

Back in the hospital he'd seem to be all right, and they'd parole him, and then they'd bring him back in off a drunken binge. Then he was psychotic, which means plumb crazy; he saw crazy visions and heard imaginary voices insulting him. He was a dangerous patient, and the doctors and attendants had to keep their eyes peeled when they were in the room with him. He seemed undernourished (as many drunks are) but the laboratory tests were all negative.

He began to refuse food and was tense and very gloomy.

He began to let himself get dirty and bullied his way into conversations and made silly speeches. Not knowing what else to do, the doctors drained his gall bladder and found it to be normal. He hid himself from the doctors and ran away again and again and got drunk. When they brought him in, he paced the room and wouldn't eat and had got down to a skeleton, weight one hundred and six pounds.

So finally in July, 1938, Doctor Charles W. Dunn remembered to do what the other doctors had neglected. Dunn examined the man's sex glands; and found that they were not much. They were what is called "hypo-plastic," that is, they were little.

Doctor Dunn's experimental treatment was simple. He started injections of testosterone propionate, twenty-five milligrams twice a week. To make a long story short, after four months of that treatment, in October, 1938, the ex-crazy man was discharged from the Delaware State Hospital. He was no longer seeing pink elephants or Brooklyn boys marching over the foot of his bed, nor hearing insulting voices. He was active and playing tennis and much more contented, and had begun putting on weight.

On this recovery he did not attempt to break parole. He wrote to Doctor Dunn in April, 1939, saying he still had spells where he felt he was somewhat inadequate. But he was doing hard physical labor now and weighed one hundred and eighty pounds.

Doctor Dunn did not pretend that testosterone was a panacea for insanity; what he offered was now that you had this pure chemical, testosterone, you could try it as a key to see if it fit this or that mysterious lock.

It is a carefully hidden tragedy in many a family that a boy fails to develop, that he's a victim of delayed adolescence; and upon such youngsters Dunn began trying out testosterone, but cautiously. The medical textbooks tell you that puberty, in general, occurs in boys between eleven and thirteen years of age, and occasionally as late as their seventeenth year. Yet it's a variable event; there are youngsters who show their sex before eleven and some stay children till beyond nineteen and then become men—without any gland treatment at all.

Dunn began giving testosterone to thin underdeveloped boys with feebly developed sex glands. They were between nine and thirteen years old. They were low in energy as well as infantile. They were no good at football, baseball, and basket ball; and their low mental energy kept them behind in their schoolwork. And they were ashamed, and felt inferior and God knows what this would do to their personalities in their later lives, even though they finally did become normal sexually.

It being chemically pure, so that you knew exactly what you were giving, Dunn found it remarkable the way he could accurately dose the testosterone. He was a good psychologist as well as a good doctor and knew the harm it might do to these boys if you gave them doses big enough to make them men at one fell swoop—the way the Johns Hopkins doctors had done with that little three-and-a-half-year-old Negro boy they were trying to cure of tumors of the larynx.

Shrewdly Doctor Dunn brought these physically and mentally laggard boys up toward the condition of their classmates with little doses of testosterone. The first effect they felt was more energy so that they could play and fight, and they tired much less easily. Gradually they began developing sexual apparatus like that of normal boys and began growing pubic hair and hair under their arms; yet on these low doses of testosterone they did not become sexually overactive, but now they were no longer ashamed after games when they went to the showers. Their resistance to smoldering infections that had always plagued them surged upward; and as they put on weight and were more and more ready to knock chips off their friends' shoulders, they became more gay and confident of tomorrow and took a higher rank in their classes.

Again, testosterone was no panacea for backward boys; but when careful physical examination showed them underdeveloped in their gonads, then Doctor Dunn gave testosterone a careful try. What Dunn was finding, like Walter Kearns, was that the effect of testosterone wasn't primarily sexual, it was constitutional.

There was a clear-cut chemical explanation for the new energy in these delayed-adolescent boys to whom Dunn gave those carefully limited doses of testosterone. In the middle and later nineteen-thirties, when the hormone-hunting pioneers were first testing it, they were principally astounded at its power to make eunuchoids go to town sexually; but now at the beginning of the nineteen-forties Doctor E. Perry McCullagh and Doctor H. R. Rossmiller of Cleveland, Ohio, discovered its terrific power on the human body's power of oxidation, its chemical fire of life.

A sexually underdeveloped young man of thirty-four had been given a new life with testosterone propionate injections; then he'd received no treatment for eleven months. Quickly he went down hill. He had developed a normal prostate gland under the testosterone treatment; now this had withered. He'd had a great boost of energy; now he was tired out after the slightest effort. And there was good chemical reason for his peplessness: his basal metabolism rate was down to nearly minus-thirty.

In July, 1940, the Cleveland doctors began giving this half-man huge doses (they'd proved it was perfectly safe) of the new methyl testosterone that he could take by mouth in the simple form of pills. Twenty pills of testosterone, two hundred milligrams a day. This tremendous medication didn't upset his digestion and had no harmful effect at all. And at the same time, within a week, his basal metabolism rate began soaring, up and up from nearly minus-thirty to plus-five and over at the end of the Summer; and he'd gone up from a hundred and forty-five pounds in weight to over one hundred and seventy, and felt fit as a fiddle. Rejuvenated.

Again and again on six other sexually retarded men Doctors McCullagh and Rossmiller confirmed this till now unsuspected power of testosterone to stoke up the chemical fire of life, to raise the basal metabolism; and yet, mysteriously, this testosterone action didn't burn up the body tissues, because, with one exception, all of these now fiery and lusty and stronger men actually put on weight.

The Cleveland hormone hunters, when they kept on giving testosterone in big enough doses and over long enough periods of time to these sexually-lacking half-men, discovered that the magic chemical did more than give them more energy and a gain in weight. It changed them, and fundamentally. Here were half-men whose arms were slender, whose chests were narrow, whose necks were thin and rounded. After many months on testosterone, their chest and shoulder muscles grew much heavier and stronger; and their neck muscles stood out against the overlying skin.

Testing it on one dwarfish sexually underdeveloped boy, they discovered that testosterone could act as an actual growth hormone when you gave enough of it for a long enough time. They tried it on a down-at-the-heel, under par little boy of nineteen. He was sickly. When he was ten he'd had spells that began with headaches, grinding his teeth, sometimes vomiting and then going into a sleep deep like a coma. No convulsions. When he was twelve, he was only forty-seven inches tall and weighed only forty-eight pounds and was definitely dwarfish. The doctors had given him thyroid; no go; then pituitary gland extract on the theory that this might set his testicles to working. No soap. Then they gave him the supposedly more powerful pituitary-like hormone from the urine of pregnant mares. No dice. Little growth. No signs of maturity. From age twelve to nineteen, he had gained five inches and now was only fifty-three inches tall.

Then at last in 1940, methyl testosterone. He began maturing sexually and shot up in height at the rate of 3.9 inches per year.

What was this mysterious chemical power of testosterone to transform the muscles of these tragically boyish half-men, and to make them stronger and to make them grow? Doctor Allan T. Kenyon of the University of Chicago found a hint of the chemical answer. Doctor Fred Koch, who'd blazed the trail for testosterone's discovery, worked with him on this adventure, and how its consequences must have pleased that modest man. For Kenyon, giving testosterone not only to eunuchoid almost-men, *but even to men who were apparently normal*, discovered that the male hormone had a power as deep, as fundamental as that of any vital chemical so far discovered.

In some mysterious manner, not yet chemically clear, testosterone caused the human body to synthesize protein, it caused the human body to be able to build the very stuff of its own life.

The revelation of these deep chemical powers of testosterone swept away all my silly thoughts of its mere sexiness. Nobody had to blush with shame at the mention of this kind of master-chemical. It was no mere aphrodisiac. It was more than a tonic for sexually nasty old men. It was a life-builder. Now it was becoming clear why formerly broken men became tough under its influence, why those melancholy men might be given, thanks to it, a bright look toward tomorrow.

I began to understand the curious transformations that testosterone brought about in certain remarkable guinea-pigs observed by the genial Doctor George N. Papanicolaou at Cornell University Medical School in New York City. When together with Doctor Emil A. Falk, he performed the highly academic experiment of castrating young male guinea-pigs before their puberty, they remained feeble muscularly; and the big bunches of muscles (which normal male guinea-pigs have at their temples) remained completely flat. Pituitary hormones, when they were injected into female guinea-pigs, caused some swelling of these muscles; but in those castrated baby males the pituitary hormone had no effect whatever. No testicles—feeble muscle.

It was clear to our professors that a guinea-pig's testicles are fundamental not only to his perpetuation but to his muscularity; and now when they injected testosterone into castrated young guinea-pigs their temple muscles quickly swelled to normal; and when they injected testosterone into female guinea-pigs their flat temple muscles became indistinguishable from those of full-grown manly males; and under testosterone these guinea-pig eunuchs and females became muscular all over their bodies.

Professor Papanicolaou gravely concluded that this experiment explained the generally higher muscular development of the male mammal; but then, highly academic man though he was, he threw out a hint of hope that testosterone might hold for one of the most terribly fatal, inexorable, and saddest diseases known to mankind.

This sickness was progressive muscular dystrophy; it runs in families; it occurs mostly in little boys; it's a horrible condition where the youngsters seem to be born healthy, and then when they're starting to toddle, they begin to weaken. There's nothing generally wrong with them except that their main muscle groups undergo degeneration, getting flabbier and flabbier so that the poor kids at first can't walk and then can hardly move at all and have to be carried around on pillows. Mercifully, before reaching manhood many of them die.

There was absolutely nothing the doctors could do about it; and only these two grim facts were known about progressive muscular dystrophy: it hits boys much oftener than girls and in a more acute form; and its terrible progress slows up a bit if the boys do manage to live till puberty.

These curious facts were a research clue for Doctor Charles L. Hoagland, at the Rockefeller Institute Hospital in New York City. At this temple of medical science, when the word is passed out that a disease is going to be scientifically studied, it is such a wonderful hospital, its scientific fame is so great that in less than no time it has plenty of patients suffering a given sickness no matter how seemingly rare. So now Doctor Charles L. Hoagland very quickly had at his disposal forty youngsters whose muscles were melting away. He promised nothing to their parents. Indeed he could hardly have done so. He told the parents he wanted to study the muscle chemistry and general chemistry of their doomed children; and so great is the faith of all fathers and mothers in science that Hoagland's merely studying it in their youngsters, even though he honestly promised them nothing, gave them a pathetic little hope.

Powerless against the grim march of this muscular disintegration, Hoagland took a Brodie on the facts that boys are the ones that usually suffer it and that it is much more acute before puberty. He put this hope into scientific words. "This . . . leads one to the hypothesis," he wrote, "that the essential aberration in progressive muscular dystrophy is one closely connected with the biological phenomenon of maleness on the one hand and, perhaps, with those systems concerned with growth and development on the other."

Then he jumped to testosterone to try to save these doomed children. His reasoning was that various vitamin and hormone chemicals of the steroid, $C_{17}H_{28}$, chemical family were developers and growers of young human beings. And by far the handiest of the steroid hormones to get, and the safest, and by far the most generally powerful was the pure male hormone, testosterone. What's more, didn't it build big muscles on guinea-pigs? So it came about that our chemical now got the remarkable scientific recognition of being admitted for test to the Rockefeller Institute Hospital and in the scientific medical world that's as high as any chemical can aspire to go.

These little boys doomed with progressive muscular dystrophy show only one chemical peculiarity—an increase in the excretion of the nitrogenous chemical, creatine, in their urine. Creatine is found in muscle and mysteriously has something to do with the power and integrity of muscle, and testosterone builds creatine up in muscle. Hoagland began injecting testosterone propionate into a few of the doomed children and then later began feeding a little group of them methyl testosterone.

Here was his very cagey preliminary conclusion, early in 1944:

"If creatine retention, which occurred as the result of testosterone medication, may be regarded as a true storage phenomenon, it would indicate that in progressive muscular dystrophy the capacity to store creatine is not irreversibly altered," wrote Hoagland.

And the ability to store creatine is fundamental to the power and integrity of muscles, so here was a gleam of hope.

Hoagland was very properly scientifically cautious, and parents whose little boys were doomed to the horrible flaccid living death of progressive muscular dystrophy would have to read very hard between the lines to catch Hoagland's implied hope.

"Moreover," he wrote, "it would justify the administration of the hormone in therapeutic amounts over a prolonged interval of time in order to learn if muscle function is improved thereby."

So here at last was testosterone, pitted as a champion against a terribly deadly disease. Now all fathers and mothers of such doomed children must be on the alert for this trial of testosterone against progressive muscular dystrophy at the Rockefeller Institute Hospital in New York City.

"Studies directed toward this end are underway, and the results will be reported in a subsequent communication," wrote Hoagland.

PART IV

TESTOSTERONE THE BUILDER

CHAPTER EIGHTEEN

IN THE adventure of testosterone, it came to me once more that the only wealth in the world is friends; you can have all the engraved pieces of paper that maybe mean wealth and security. You can even take my health away, okay, so long as I've friends, they'll fight for my life and bring it back; and if they don't, their fighting for it will have made the whole show worth-while. You can break my spirit and show up the fears that are always close to the surface in me, all right, so long as there are true friends, they'll understand it and tell me "to get back in there, for Christ's sake, and stick and slug," as Herman Bundesen says it in his special Chicago slang. This present wrassle to get at the truth about testosterone has depended upon two of the toughest friends I have in the world though they in no way collaborated to get me into this, nor have they worked together to keep up my nerve to stay at it. The adventure was sparked by one of these friends while the other one at that time hardly knew the word, testosterone. But when the project was in danger of flopping from my faint-heartedness, the remarkable personal experience of this second friend, with testosterone, really gave me the nerve to see the story through to the finish.

He gave me the feeling of to hell with consequences. The danger I sensed was my enthusiasm for the life-building power of the pure male hormone. Enthusiasm is the enemy of intellect. There was my expansiveness to worry about and then, too, my buck fever at letting myself go, in cold type, on the possibility of testosterone's giving men a new lease on life. It was my fear of the responsibility.

Though both of these friends are doctors, neither of them is professionally an organic chemist or even a hormone hunter. The first of them, Herman Bundesen, started me on the project originally, getting me going by the tall statement that just as there are chemicals that renew worn-out soil, so there may be chemicals to renew the vigor of worn-out men. But why? It might be a purely poetic fancy. Who was Bundesen to say it? I believe he'd flunk the examination if an organic chemistry professor would ask him to write the steroid structural formula of testosterone. He belonged not to that vivisecting, hormone-hunting crew of biologists who cut this or that gland out of animals and then learnedly note what happens.

If I'd have put Bundesen's hunch about the existence of any chemical renewing slipping men to the judgment of the great vivisector, Professor Anton J. Carlson, he would have blown both of us off the earth with his mighty question—

"*Verr* iss de effidence?"

And yet I had absolute confidence in Bundesen. He was just tough, practical old Herman, his face deeply chiseled by his hard life, yet looking far too young for his years and the life he had led, with far too much fighting heart left after all the years the Chicago boys (as Hemingway calls them) had been trying to tear that heart out of him. There was Herman who could be so tough and mean and who had a heart like a washtub. So when, despite Herman's ignorance in the Carlsonian, professorial sense, he hinted that there was at last a chemical that might give some older guys a new lease on life, I listened and then took a long close look at him.

Then I said okay, I'd believe him—enough to roll up my sleeves and spit on my hands and start the scientific literature-digging job of finding out if what he said was really so. That's the Dutch for you. Worse than the man from Missouri.

What with the public health three-ringed circus he runs, I

couldn't imagine how Bundesen found time to get his head around this new science; he's a super factory manager of safe mass production of life, new life; he's a rough-and-tumble death-fighting type and no scholar. Yet now, after months of studying hundreds of organic-chemical, hormone-hunting and clinical publications in English, German, and French, after months of digesting them and distilling them down into a long abstract that would make a book much bigger than this one you're now reading, it did begin to seem as if testosterone might have something of the life-renewing magic for men that Herman claimed for it.

Having got my head around all this information, even then I didn't quite believe Herman's hints of its power. I'll never forget the day he gave me those first tablets, little ten milligram pills not much bigger than an aspirin, for my own use. No part of a new lease on life could hide in pills so negligible. I looked at Bundesen just the least bit quizzically and saw his old, tanned, rough-hewn, youthful face and watched him, still raring to go after a terrible day of fighting the Washington red-tape boys, a day that had my own tail really dragging.

"Okay, I'll try them," I said to Herman.

Now I'd been on them a year, faithfully; and it seemed as if there was a bit of an up in my spirits, a bit more optimism, maybe, and yet, and yet, wasn't it all what the pessimistic doctors call suggestion?

I mulled back over my notes and had to admit that in the deepest biological sense testosterone had authentic power. It could make hens crow and act like roosters; it could transform feeble and fuzzy-witted eunuchoid humans into alert and hard-working males; it could put a healthy tan on human skin that was wrinkled and old and gray and pasty; it could make certain dwarfish boys grow into nearly normal young men; it could actually spark the human body's building of indispensable proteins; it could swell and harden feeble and flabby muscles in eunuchoid men as well as in guinea-pigs; it could (so Walter Kearns hinted) put sap of life into certain aging men. But wasn't this last all a flash in the pan?

I have great respect, believe it or not, for medical authority. And now when I consulted the Report of the Council on Pharmacy and Chemistry of the American Medical Association for May 13, 1939, what I read in it dampened my spirits considerably.

"Therapy (with testosterone)," the report said, "has been attempted in the following conditions; and, while the treatment of all of them is still in the experimental stage, it appears that the results are promising in only a few."

Some of "the following conditions" had to do with the possibility of a new lease on life for men who were aging.

The judgment of the Council (made up of unquestionably eminent authorities) was austere. "Reliable evaluation of benefits or dangers must await extensive experimentation over a period of years. . . . All other claims are either exaggerated or premature," the report said, "and should be disregarded until substantial evidence becomes available on which to evaluate them."

When any new chemical or vaccine or serum is really the life-giving McCoy, the Council sanctifies it by listing it in its New and Non-official Remedies. And now the Council, ominously, "deferred consideration of testosterone propionate until it has been properly evaluated by ample clinical experience."

One of the pioneers on the trail of testosterone in making men of almost-men or broken men was Professor J. B. Hamilton, now of Yale University. And now, in the 1942 edition of the American Medical Association's book, *Glandular Physiology* and *Therapy*, this unquestioned authority was bearish about certain uses of testosterone.

Professor Hamilton warned us to distinguish the effects of senility from those that can be properly accredited to testis (testicle) insufficiency. Hadn't enthusiasts for testosterone put altogether too much stress on the importance of testicles in preventing the breakdown of the rest of the human body as men grow old?

"This has led to the deplorable and perhaps wishful thought that restoration of testis function produces rejuvenation."

Rejuvenation was certainly a fighting word even to the best qualified hormone hunters.

Professor Hamilton admitted that testosterone had that curious power to make old men, some old men, feel like singing "Oh, what a beautiful morning." It is the condition that is medically known as euphoria. It is a kind of derogatory medical word for a feeling of bodily comfort, well-being, an absence of pain or distress. For men who are arriving at the stage of old pots or crocks this euphoria is not common or natural; and, vaguely, the good doctors are likely to be suspicious about it. Paretics, in the first stages of their brain syphilis, show euphoria notably, and then there was that lamentable experience of old Brown-Séquard. Beware of euphoria!

Professor Hamilton warned: "Euphoria is not uncommon (from testosterone) and should be guarded against by the strict insurance that the patient does not over-exert."

Old men, for God's sake, should act their age, with due regard to David and Solomon's having budgeted them to three score years and ten. "Stimulation of an older man with testosterone may cause him to feel younger and attempt to lead the life of a younger man," wrote Doctor Hamilton.

"The situation is somewhat like that of pouring new wine into old bottles," said the professor. And every student of the Bible knows what happened to those unfortunate bottles.

Testosterone (except for its effect upon eunuchoids) was still definitely an upstart in the highest medical circles. I, myself, had been roughed around good and plenty by the highest medical circles for jumping the gun (so those circles said) on such developments as the one-day fever-chemical treatment of early, contagious syphilis. That was all right; that was all coming out in the wash; and I might make monkeys of these high medical circles on that one, but there was a far greater danger in telling a gun-jumping story about testosterone . . . Shades of Ponce de Leon. . . . Poor old Brown-Séquard. . . . When you've got to get old, you've got to get old. . . . And the one danger I feared more than any other was that of being made ridiculous.

So now I began to sabotage testosterone to myself, mentally, taking every scientific report of its possible power to rebuild old life with more than a grain of salt. The high medical circles had me buffaloed. Better lay off this one, brother, I began telling myself, lying awake nights with the surf booming on the beach at Wake Robin.

Then the second of my dear friends, Doctor E. J. O'Brien, had his severe spine operation, and that indirectly led to his putting new fire in me go on with the adventure of testosterone.

Like all O'Briens who are fighters and worthy to bear that ancient name, Doctor Edward J. O'Brien is Pat O'Brien to you. He is a chest surgeon in Detroit, Michigan; and as a thoracic surgeon, can look knife-men like Harold Brunn, Evarts Graham, John Alexander, Edward D. Churchill, and all prominent chest surgeons in the eye and stand up to them on even terms doing chest operations. Than that, in this particular surgical discipline, you can say no more.

This, you are right in objecting, does not qualify Pat O'Brien as an authority on testosterone as a revigorator of men. But neither have I ever been one of those specialty worshippers who think that because a man is good at cutting out lungs, he's a monkey about any other part of the body. What qualified Pat O'Brien as an observer of the human body for me was that he is white-hot honest, has a superb disregard for mere medical authority, has a profound belief that medical science hasn't begun to scratch the surface in improving on the down-at-the-heel condition of man as God left him after the creation, and, finally, that he is skeptical about all new science and hard-boiled about weighing its claims.

I had got to know Pat O'Brien closely because we had been through one tough death-fighting war together. From the beginning of our working together, I discovered that although it was surgery which had made him internationally famous, from which he got his bread and butter, yet Pat, far over and beyond being a surgeon, is a public healthman, fighting to make his bloody cutting, tatting and crocheting of the human body no longer necessary. For many years his special death-fighting field has been the surgical treatment of tuberculosis. Remarkably, though a surgeon, he has a grasp of the basic way to eradicate TB, a grasp deeper than that of any bacteriologist or medical or public healthman I've ever known.

To Pat the TB fight is no mere science, it is religion. He is fanatical; and his fierceness against the white plague makes polite public healthmen and decorous dignitaries of the National Tuberculosis Association squirm a bit while he utters his blasts against the waxy TB microbe.

O'Brien is a great natural actor and snarls and growls, walking up and down the floor, giving you the guts of how to wipe out this curse in little words that are for all that scientific.

"TB is a communicable disease and everyone who has it gets it from somebody else. Its eradication is very simple. If all who have it are found, isolated, and properly treated, the disease will cease to exist."

And for Pat this is no mere crusading battle cry. In Detroit and in all of Michigan Pat O'Brien *is* the TB death fight. Working with him in the Detroit TB campaign in the middle and late nineteen-thirties, I've watched him do four big tough de-ribbing operations on far-gone TB victims in one morning and then taper off with twelve phrenic operations to paralyze the diaphragms and rest the TB-infected lungs of early cases. I've heard him tell Detroit's city fathers, Wayne County's budget-balancing auditors and Detroit's industrial big-shots that the prevailing public health penny-pinching, not giving every Detroit citizen a chance for TB diagnosis by a free chest film, is perpetuating murder. It's worse than murder, really; it's the silliest false economy, because by finding all the tuberculosis and curing it in its early stages you'd wipe out the annual millions of dollars it now costs to maintain the far-gone tuberculous sick.

In those brave days of the late nineteen-thirties, O'Brien already was at the top of his stride, not scared of God nor man nor the medical profession. He'd denounced chiseling doctors; he'd threaten exposure (almost unheard of in the high ethical medical world) of an incompetent physician who had let a patient rot to death with TB for lack of early and proper treatment.

There were plenty who would have liked to have taken Pat for a Chicago ride, or at the least, to have read him out of the County Medical Society; but he was too competent; and fearless; and knew where the bodies were buried.

That was Pat O'Brien at the beginning of the nineteen-forties, the spearhead in making the TB fight in Detroit and Michigan a model for the world, with the TB death rate in Detroit, despite the war's dislocations and all those tuberculous Negroes coming in, below that of any other large American city. Pat was tops as a chest surgeon, growling at his crack operating team, "Let's go, boys, let's go," and doing the terrific operation of taking out a lung in record time.

Then he fell upon evil days.

His back went back on him. For years he'd been driving in rain and sleet and snow all over Michigan, inspecting state TB sanatoria, operating at Kalamazoo, Battle Creek, Pontiac,

Gaylord, and Saginaw, Michigan, and Lima, Ohio, urging legislative action for more TB beds, driving while he wool-gathered new public health campaigns. Twice Providence had seen him through smash-ups with the car completely demolished, and both times Pat pulled out of the wrecks with a broken back but still living. Now all this had caught up with him, leaving him with a terrible atrophic arthritis of his lower spine so that it was agony to operate or even to get up out of a chair. He operated and walked, bent over; and it was pitiful to see him.

The Michigan TB fight missed Pat's spirit. His old energy disintegrated against his constant pain. Favoring his back, his leg muscles had wasted. He'd shopped around by airplane to many of the top orthopedic surgeons all over America—who agreed that the vertebrae of the lower part of his spine should be fused.

He ended up under the care of Doctor Fremont A. Chandler, of Chicago, who operated upon him. Yet Chandler was worried, wouldn't promise Pat a thing. After all, O'Brien was along in his fifties and his muscles were atrophied and flabby, and there was a doubt that he could develop them.

Just the same, eighteen days after his operation, Pat O'Brien got out of bed with his fused lower spine and the next week walked into the coat room at Harper Hospital in Detroit under his own steam. And now, when I saw him just a few weeks later, already back at work, it was a new Pat O'Brien. The operation had been a brilliant success, but that wasn't all, that was only half of it.

That night Pat amazed me. "You know, Paul," he said, "if I had my medical life to live over, I wouldn't go in for chest surgery. I wouldn't be in this TB fight. I'd concentrate on endocrinology. . . . Now, take this testosterone. . . ."

What the devil did Pat know about testosterone? Mind you, he didn't know that right then I was deep in the testos-terone adventure and worried about going on with it. Excited, I looked Pat O'Brien in the eye. "What do you mean, testosterone?" I asked.

There was a healthy tanned color to his face; there was the old fire in his fierce blue eyes; it was the Pat of old. "You remember how I was before Chandler operated, a wreck?" he asked. "You remember my calf muscles, flabby and atrophied?"

Then he got up and as a demonstration, straight as a soldier, he walked fast up and down the room. He came back to me. "Feel those thigh muscles now!" he said. "Feel those calf muscles!"

They were hard like a runner's.

"And you think they've come back that way just because my back's better so I don't have to favor 'em?" Pat asked. "Don't be silly. I haven't had enough exercise to develop anything."

"What's done it, Pat?" I stooged him.

"Testosterone," he said. "This testosterone propionate. That's what's done it. The day before the operation they began giving me shots of it, and it has definitely helped me in building new muscle and bone.

Today Pat's on the job again, full time, operating. Today he's again got the pot of the Michigan TB fight bubbling. He's the old Pat, agitating a new state-wide TB case-finding fight to uncover every undetected early tuberculous sick man and woman in Michigan.

CHAPTER NINETEEN

IN ANY fight it isn't the statistics of the power you've got on your side or the power that's against you that determines your conduct in battle. It's the kind of men you know you've got fighting shoulder to shoulder with you, since in all modern wars, little or big, life is now so organized that you do not fight alone. Now in this adventure of telling the story of testosterone I knew I couldn't be luckier, because here were Herman Bundesen and Pat O'Brien believing in testosterone and absolutely trusting me to fight down my native enthusiasm and tell the story as fairly and truly as it could be told. This morning, far away from both of them, looking out over Lake Michigan, gray but still gentle, in early December, I don't feel alone at all; it's as if Herman and Pat are both here looking over my shoulder.

I woolgather out to the misty mysterious horizon and ponder that it takes all kinds of men to make up mankind's fight for life. In our sad yet dimly hopeful struggle to be longer-lived and stronger we need all of the one hundred and thirty thousand doctors we've got in this country, though we could use many more better doctors and more doctors too, God knows. Especially we could use many more organic chemists. But we have to work with what we've got, and what have we?

We've got a rank and file who are exactly as average as any other profession, like plumbers, garage mechanics or undertakers. They, the rank and file, are not doctors from an inborn or inspired passion to fight death and make life stronger; they're doctors because it's a job in a high-placed profession; they're definitely in the doctoring *business*—or otherwise they wouldn't, as an organization, be howling so loudly about the practice of medicine, as a private enterprise, being taken over by the government. (Not that such a move would make the doctors any better.) Doctoring is not generally religious. The rank and file are not hot about new life-saving discovery. If they were, they'd be building bonfires in the street and holding guild parades over the terrific death-fighting success of such new remedies as the sulfas or penicillin.

Then there is a smaller group of highly technically competent men, specialists, marvelous at plumbing your bladder, wizards at tinkering with your brain, able to open your chest without too big a chance of killing you, analyzing the machinery of your heart and making a pretty good guess about how long you've got to live and pretty honest about their modest ability to make your heart last much longer. These specialists groove themselves pretty deeply, are extremely cagey about sticking their necks out beyond their own little corner of the body; and their teamwork in tackling the troubles of the human body as a whole is still pretty feebly developed.

In their own special disciplines they're pretty much on their toes regarding operations and forms of treatment that are orthodox and have "gone through the crucible of the clinic" as one doctor put it. Yet the majority of them are not looking for new wrinkles to lift human life higher or to save it. They are mostly progressive in Boss Kettering's sense: "Anything new is perfectly all right so long as it's just like the old way of doing it."

Every new medical discovery has got to pass its test with these competent specializing medical men; and it is not only the intrinsic merit of the discovery that determines the issue. In the first place, the discovery has to cross the hurdle of being new—that's a tough one. Then the discovery faces another danger—it is a trait deep and dark in the hearts of men and not confined at all to doctors. It is what the Germans call "schadenfreude"—a malicious joy at another's loss. . . . "So Zilch thought he had a heart tonic in this new testosterone? Well, we certainly tripped him up on that one. . . ."

This hatred of a discovery that you haven't made yourself operates to frustrate and slow down many a medical advance. Nobody knows how much human misery persists unnecessarily; nobody can count how many lives have been lost because of this curious human reflex of negativism. Again Boss Kettering puts it in homely words: "I didn't make the discovery myself so it can't be so."

Now over and beyond the immense medical rank and file and the lesser group of what we may call the conservative technically competent there are a few lone-wolf exploring men. Among them, in this instance of the progress of testosterone, are Herman Bundesen and Pat O'Brien. There is a certain spirit that characterizes both of them. It is simply that they hate to see anybody die, or anybody suffer who doesn't have to, granted that science does exist—or *may* exist—to save them.

They have the opposite of schadenfreude; they say hooray to discovery.

They make many mistakes because they will try everything, including remedies that on the face of them are surely unscientific and foolish. In the academic sense they are simple men, really primitive, because they do not know their limitations. Just because Herman Bundesen is the world's greatest public health fighter for the lives of mothers and newborn babies, that doesn't exclude him from trying to revigorate an aging man with testosterone. Just because Pat O'Brien is the world's most determined enemy of the needless, shameful curse of tuberculosis, he is not ashamed to stick his neck out, scientifically, on the muscle-building power of the pure male hormone.

Now it was wonderful for me to have a pat on the back from men like O'Brien and Bundesen because testosterone was going to be different. It was not a life-or-death, yes-or-no chemical like the sulfas or penicillin, where the prevention of microbic murder is so clear-cut that nobody can deny it. Though even here in special instances of certain highly incurable or inexorably fatal infections there are some strange untold stories of these magic chemicals having to get their test by the back doors of medical schools, and even in the actual scientific black market in the case of penicillin's cure of hitherto incurable sub-acute bacterial endocarditis.

But testosterone's hurdles were tougher. It wasn't whether the pure male hormone was going to be tested to determine whether a man lived or died, right now. It was whether he'd feel better or not better after testosterone; it wasn't like here a microbe, now not a microbe; for testosterone it was difficult to establish what the good hard-boiled medical specialists call objective criteria of improvement or cure; if testosterone had anything to do with life or death you'd know in a generation, and research grants aren't made for that length of time.

Then at the same time testosterone was going to get a real going over from the schadenfreude boys because, biologically, its action seemed to be so widespread and deep in the human body. What the hell did this male hormone think it was anyway? A builder of protoplasm? A synthesizer of proteins? That alone made it suspect. The schadenfreude boys don't like any but little modest discoveries. Testosterone—body-builder? To any soberly scientific man (those organic chemists excepted, and weren't they all a bit crazy?) there could be no such single chemical animal.

Living machinery isn't that simple. A single chemical with that much power smacked of the bad word, elixir. The dictionary says: "Elixir: An imaginary cordial supposed to be capable of sustaining life indefinitely."

You may be sure the medical highbrow smear-boys would be waiting to give the business to any doctor foolhardy enough to experiment widely with the possible life-restoring action of testosterone upon sick older men. The experimenter might only claim that it seemed to sustain life somewhat; the smear-boys would guffaw and kill the work by implying that this new elixir was intended to sustain life indefinitely. A dirty word, elixir.

You would have to be a bold and an ignorant prober to pit testosterone against the diseases of the middle life of men, the troubles of their blood vessels and hearts and nervous systems, diseases of unknown causation, they were called. You'd have to be theoretically out of the orthodox medical groove, maybe better yet, not a theorizer at all, but just a medical bumpkin who'd try anything. It might help you to be a bad theorizer, like George Minot, who based his marvelous liver treatment of deadly pernicious anemia on very dubious logic; or like Manfred Sakel who discovered the insulin shock cure of dementia praecox on theoretical grounds that were not only silly but mystical. If you were going after the big diseases of the middle life of men, with testosterone, you had better be simple; it would help you to be scientifically illiterate, as the learned medical school professors say.

Doctor Heinz Arndt, of Koenigsberg in East Prussia, must have been that kind of man. Shortly after testosterone became commercially available in the late nineteen-thirties, this Arndt, about whom I can find nothing personal, what with the war, must have asked himself some pretty fundamental questions.

Is hunger for the male hormone confined to those unfortunates whose sex glands have been lost or have remained undeveloped?

Probably not. Arndt had one fact to go on. The natural production of the male hormone declines in men as they grow older. That could be demonstrated, not too accurately, by finding less and less of the male hormone's waste product, androsterone, in the urine of older men.

Granted that less and less male hormone as men grew older might mean less and less total vitality. Then Arndt went off the deep end. He must have put himself a question that had no justification according to the standard orthodox textbooks of medicine or hormone hunting. It was the rankest kind of speculation. Arndt, uncluttered up and uninhibited by the big textbook boys that you didn't find in the provincial town of Koenigsberg, must have asked himself a really wild question. . . .

Mightn't a gradually developing, insidious hidden hunger for the male hormone be responsible for certain major diseases of the heart, the blood vessels, the brain of apparently normal men in their middle or later years of life?

You could test that question, Arndt knew, because now you had the crystal-pure male hormone, testosterone. A clear-cut weapon to give you a maybe clear-cut answer, yes or no. Arndt was innocent of one prejudice that seemed to confuse orthodox hormone hunters. Many of these authorities seemed to think that for something to be out of whack with a man's male hormone production, a man shouldn't have any testicles at all. It is plain that Arndt had the common sense to see that a man *might* have perfectly normal-looking testicles that weren't doing their stuff, chemically. Who knew what was really going on in any pair of testicles just by looking at them or feeling them? Nobody.

I know nothing about this Heinz Arndt except what he reveals of himself in his one publication in the *Wiener Medizinische Wochenschrift*, but he must have been a young and simple man, because he drew a long bow, now beginning his attempted rescue of certain ailing middle-aged and older men. He shoved off on his adventure by stating that it had been known for hundreds of years, by observation of castration of domestic animals, that the sex glands do not limit their effect to sexual function. They act upon the entire animal, particularly upon its psychic condition. This was a bad start. How measure changes in psychic condition—objectively?

Heinz Arndt forgot the sex angle of testosterone. He simply began throwing it at some of the most formidable diseases of middle age, pretty nearly every disturbance of middle-aged men that you'll find in the books. He cut off a big chunk of experiment, bigger than any one man could possibly chew. He entitled his scientific paper "On the Therapy of Extra-genital Disturbances with the Sex Hormones."

Arndt started shooting testosterone propionate into a forty-nine-year-old merchant who was a psychasthenic and had terrible pains over his heart and had shopped around to many doctors with no result. He shot ten milligrams of testosterone into this man's buttocks twice a week; and after fourteen days, the man felt "much fresher and more able to work." He kept on with the injections and then started giving the man methyl testosterone by mouth, very small doses, only five milligrams a day. After some weeks, the man reported he was okay, could work full time again. Appetite good and sleeping well. No more heart pains. "I feel like an entirely different man," he said.

It sounded like a patent medicine testimonial.

But the complaints of all of Arndt's patients were not so vague. He tried testosterone on a fifty-seven-year-old locksmith who was suffering from severe obliterative disease of the blood vessels of his legs and feet. He couldn't walk a hundred yards without terrific pains in his calf muscles. At night his leg cramps were so bad he couldn't sleep. His toes were bluish from his interrupted blood circulation. X ray films showed calcification of the arteries of his feet, and his feet were always cold. Not very long after Arndt had begun daily shots of testosterone propionate, that man came back reporting that he could sleep again. "It feels as if the blood can run in my feet again," he said. As the treatment went on, his feet got warmer and became pink in color, and they were much less painful. Then, too, there were no longer those cramps in his calves after walking, and pretty soon the man reported complete disappearance of pain. He was working full time.

Arndt gave the pure male hormone to seventeen men, several of them with this same arterial obliterative disease of their legs and feet, several with the severe chest pains of angina pectoris, others with blood vessel disease of their brains, unable to concentrate mentally, attempting suicide, profoundly melancholic, nervously exhausted; in general, they were past fifty, some of them nearly seventy, a couple of them were still in their thirties. They were all a human rearguard suffering from damaged blood circulation of their legs or hearts or brains. They had all shopped around medically, and they had all given up hope.

They were a rag-tag-and-bobtail of humanity ready for life's scrap pile or already on it. The fierce pains over their hearts, the cramps in their legs, their nervous breakdowns had resisted all modern treatment. Now after testosterone, and only testosterone, they were all (with one exception who'd got better and then relapsed) free of their pains and depression and sleeping well again and eating and working. In all seventeen cases in detail Arndt described the history of their downhill journey, of how one saw death before his eyes, of how another had attempted suicide because of his pain, of how another had epileptiform attacks and loss of memory—of how gradually they came back to strong life, after testosterone.

Arndt admitted that he could add a number of cases to this seventeen in which the male hormone had had no good effect at all. But in his report he summed it all up by saying that among these men whose disease had been refractory to other treatment, testosterone had brought about a "dauerheilung," a long sustained healing. He believed that these results "demanded that further investigation be made in this field."

The war came and drew a curtain over German medical science. Arndt, himself, fades from the hormone picture. A medical cynic, or even a hard-boiled and impartial medical observer, could properly object that you could probably find the same kind of series of remarkable "cures" in a radio advertisement of the late old Doctor Goat-gland Brinkley.

As to these resurrected men, nobody knows what has become of them or whether any of them are now alive or whether testosterone permanently helped them or whether they relapsed after it was withdrawn or whether they got better again after treatment with the male hormone was resumed.

It bothered me about Arndt that he hadn't published his negative results. I remembered that there is a lunatic fringe of doctors in Germany as in all other countries. When a powerful new synthetic chemical appears on the market they're likely to try it out on every disease from housemaid's knee to incurable cancer. I recalled that when the first sulfa began working its magic against the streptococcus, the German doctors first reporting those unbelievable cures of people dying with streptococcus blood-poisoning, there were other German doctors claiming that the sulfa was saving people from fatal Hodgkin's disease, which was utterly ridiculous. I might argue in Arndt's favor that his report appeared in one of the greatest medical journals in the world, the *Wiener Medizinische Wochenschrift*. It was also true that Arndt was not boosting testosterone as a rejuvenator, since in only one case did he mention impotence and then say that this man was brought back to new sexual life. But finally German medical science was falling upon evil days, infected by the systematic lying of the Nazis; it would be comforting to find some confirmation about testosterone's power to mend the ills of older men, coming from a country where there was more respect for simple truth.

It made me feel a bit easier, finding news of testosterone

experiments upon ailing older men as reported by the distinguished French physician, Guy Laroche. He could hardly be
a quack, because he has been referred to as an authority in
one of the American Medical Association's stern warnings
about over-enthusiasm on the subject of testosterone. What
made me feel more confident in Guy Laroche was that he
recorded *quantitative*, objective, precise effects of testosterone upon older men.

"The favorable effects found on aged subjects treated with
salts of testosterone for various reasons . . ." wrote Laroche,
"have attracted our attention by their regularity."

Guy Laroche and his helpers, H. Simmonet, E. Bompard
and J. A. Huet, certainly started off with a whoop for testosterone's power to bring these oldsters back to life. Old
men, extremely fatigued, got back their forces after several
days or several weeks of treatment; their intelligence appeared more lively; their skin lost its withered look so characteristic of senility and took on a rosy color; their weight
increased; the majority of the sick old men declared that they
could urinate better and with a stronger stream. That outstanding improvement in their lives seemed to be due to a
greater strength of contraction of the muscles, not only of
their bladders, but of their diaphragm and abdominal wall.

These were all pretty strong but general statements, and
it pleased me now that Laroche had the hard-boiled determi-
nation to reduce this apparent resurrection to measurement in
exact figures. These older men, mind you, were none of them
gravely sick like those far-gone Germans. In various degrees
they suffered rheumatism or general fatigue, physical or mental, and various symptoms that you could put down as being
due to simple senility. The seven men studied by Laroche
were from fifty-three to seventy-one years old.

Treating them with testosterone, the French scientists
measured before, during, and after, the condition of their
muscular and mental reactions. They tested the old men's

muscle power on a dynamometer; they made exact mental tests of their memory and recognition of associated words, their memory by recitation and their logical intelligence by a special apparatus at the laboratory of physiology at the Henri-Rouselle Hospital. Muscle power increased in all of them, and it went up on an average of thirty-two per cent above what it had been before testosterone. Their mental sharpness showed an upsurge, too, in every one of them. Their ability to cipher, to define abstract words, to perform the tricks of intelligence tests, went up in all of them so that you could put it down in figures.

These scientific results convinced Guy Laroche that the old men weren't fooling themselves when they told the doctors how much better they were feeling, generally.

Old Man No. 1, sixty-six years old, had bad spells of dizziness and arterial disease of his feet and his hands. Fifteen injections of testosterone propionate and these symptoms and signs vanished.

Old Man No. 2, sixty-eight years old, had prostate trouble, spinal arthritis and was generally senile. Ditto injections of testosterone. There was a marked improvement in his general state of health; he became more lively and interested in life, and more active.

Old Man No. 3, sixty years old, was terrifically depressed, and couldn't work any longer as an accountant because he made continual mistakes in his calculations and suffered intense mental fatigue after a short spell of working. Ditto testosterone. There was striking improvement, physically, mentally, and in his spirit.

Two of the old men were severely rheumatic, and one of these had chronic deforming arthritis in all his joints with particularly painful swelling in both his knees. The improvement in both of these rheumatic men was unmistakable. The upsurge of physical and mental strength and in what you might call the total vitality in all of the seven men treated with testosterone was clear and definite.

Then came bad news. They'd all been built up for a letdown by the testosterone injections.

"Their improvement was clear-cut in all these fields," wrote Guy Laroche, "but it is in place to remark that it was only temporary."

This would have bothered me if their relapse into senility had occurred while the testosterone treatment was continuing. But that wasn't what happened. They all began sliding downhill again after the end of the series of fifteen testosterone injections.

This you'd expect, and it was an indirect, partial proof of testosterone's power. Testosterone doesn't pretend to make new sex glands out of old ones. It's pure and simple *substitution* treatment. Testosterone pinch hits for absent or ailing or aging testicles. What it really does is give you a pair of chemical crutches. It only gives the body, at the very best, a chemical power that healthy testicles ordinarily give it. Testosterone does not cure male hormone hunger; and if such a hormone hunger exists, it will only be satisfied so long as you keep giving the testosterone. Just as diabetics have to go on taking insulin indefinitely, so these seven old men, revived by Laroche, would have to have gone on taking testosterone to maintain for long the new life he had given them.

It was a mean experiment on the old men. Guy Laroche gave them this boost in 1938 at a time when the male hormone was still terrifically expensive; and methyl testosterone, that could be taken by mouth, hadn't yet appeared on the market. Laroche didn't so much as mention the possibility of keeping these poor old fellows on a higher step of life indefinitely. So they remained simply seven historic human experimental animals. For a few weeks they had felt a haunting return of their better days.

For a little while they were eased of pain, they could think more sharply, they walked more easily, they could work again. Laroche, probing for testosterone's effect on their total vitality, mentioned a sexual effect in one of them.

This old man of sixty-nine was senile, exhausted, rheumatic, and impotent. He complained of powerful erections such as he hadn't experienced for years. He said the erections annoyed him.

Now the experiment was over; and, so far as I know, the seven old men drifted back into their old-age shadow. Laroche boiled his results down to what he called a primordially important question—

"Is testosterone treatment favorable or not favorable to the senile organism?"

Laroche answered his own question with the proper scientific caginess, hedging a bit, leaving himself an out for which you can't blame him considering how new testosterone then was and how pitifully little the greatest searchers yet know about the human mystery. Answering his own question Laroche said: "One cannot conclude in a decisive fashion from the results obtained in the subjects of our experiment."

"However," Laroche went on, "it seems that the improvement obtained in weight, in muscular force, and in the mental state should be regarded as a sign of revigoration of the senile organism."

I'll say however.

Then Laroche admitted that this new lease on life didn't have to be so cruelly temporary—if you kept on giving testosterone.

"Clinical results observed elsewhere (in another experiment) for two years and a half, in subjects treated for prostate trouble," said Laroche, "have demonstrated the safety of the treatment and the persistence of the general revigoration."

Laroche had a feeling that this new testosterone was T.N.T. We'd better take it easy. "This augmentation in physical and mental power demands for the old man a certain prudence in its use," he said. "In what concerns the old man's general activity as well as the genital."

It seemed to follow from this warning that Laroche had observed actual sexual revigoration in other old men besides the sixty-nine-year-old man who complained of those annoying erections. Laroche gave old men who might want to be gay a sensible warning. "The senile organism carries in it organic deficiencies and fragilities that the genital hormone obviously cannot suppress," he said.

He was warning them to act their age and not to chase the girls around in Paris.

All the while I was studying this pathetic record of the temporary revigoration of the seven old men, it kept haunting me that I had seen no mention of this particular scientific publication by the American Medical Association's Council on Pharmacy and Chemistry, when the Council declared testosterone "not acceptable for New and Non-official Remedies." And yet it kept haunting me, too, that in this same decision, Guy Laroche had been quoted, in this warning which told doctors, in effect, not to get too excited about testosterone and the wild claims commercially made for it.

So I went back to the report of the Council's decision, *Journal of American Medical Association*, May 13, 1939. Yes, sure enough, two papers by Guy Laroche were referred to by the Council to bolster up its adverse decision. One to the effect that Laroche had injected testosterone into several aged men and failed to improve their sexual power appreciably; the other to the effect that testosterone does not actually shrink the prostate gland in old men with prostate trouble, but only relieves the inflammation and congestion.

But did the Council mention this particular publication by Laroche on the revigoration of the seven old men? No. Not a word of it. Though, mind you, Laroche's publication had appeared one year before the Council's adverse decision and in the scientifically respectable *Bulletin* of the Academy of Medicine in Paris.

This was a hint of the tough time testosterone was going to have to become medically reputable. It was a bit rough on Laroche, this quoting him against testosterone, jerking him out of his context, mentioning two of his scientific papers and ignoring the third which recorded testosterone's power of revigoration as shown by tests that were quantitative and objective.

This curious conduct of the Council on Pharmacy and Chemistry was the best of lessons to me.

CHAPTER TWENTY

My RESPONSIBILITY as a reporter demanded that I pay special attention to the negative results or the possible evil effects of testosterone upon men who were drifting into life's Autumn, millions of men who were pathetically eager to stay a while longer in the warm glow of life's late Summer. Despite the warnings of these highest medical authorities, just the same, many physicians, and more of them all the time, were trying out testosterone on this, that, and almost every disease of the middle and the later years of the lives of men. While that German's, Heinz Arndt, report had sounded a bit like a patent medicine testimonial, yet now experiments on testosterone's possible power to help this or that serious crack-up in older men were pouring out of clinics and hospitals in our own country. Arndt had recorded that the male hormone had eased the heart pains of his forlorn human rearguard, yet for Arndt testosterone was such a widely acting elixir that it was hard to take him seriously. But now the possible effect of the pure male hormone upon angina pectoris was being recorded in a number of serious scientific publications.

Angina pectoris is not a definite heart disease but rather a blanket name for a set of painful symptoms. This agony is the heart's signal that its muscles are starved for blood as the result of different types and degrees of blocking of the blood pump's vital arteries that nourish its muscles. Heart diseases are well-known to be one of the master-killers of men of middle life and past it. If testosterone did definitely ease or abolish the frightful pain called angina pectoris, might that mean that our vital chemical had a really fundamentally good effect on the heart's condition? If that were the case, would it follow that testosterone could actually not only increase the total vitality of men, but also maybe somewhat prolong their lives?

This was certainly a key question, a desperately serious proposition involving the hopes and fears of millions of middle-aged and older men. And it seemed imperative to me, realizing this responsibility, to put testosterone's worst foot forward. No expansiveness here, brother. Cold water here on the well-known de Kruif enthusiasm. False hopes raised here over this stern issue of life or death will make you look bad when you present your case to good old Saint Peter.

That's why I particularly studied the experiments on the effect of testosterone on angina pectoris, made by the distinguished heart specialist, Doctor Samuel A. Levine, of Boston, Massachusetts. Doctor Levine was an Assistant Professor of Internal Medicine at Harvard University and a member of that august body of doctors, The Association of American Physicians. It was obvious that he had no prejudice against testosterone. He had read reports that testosterone aided the blood supply of the arteries of the skin among people suffering from disease of the blood vessels of their legs and feet.

Mightn't it improve the blood supply of the heart itself, by widening its vessels in people whose hearts were starved for blood, and showing that starvation by the agony of angina pectoris?

Good observer that he was, Doctor Levine was tough about the time he chose to make his experiment. He gave his testosterone injections to angina pectoris sufferers during the late Fall and Winter, because that's the time when they suffer these pains most severely. Any remedy you'd try out in the Spring would be open to question if it seemed to ease that horrible pain, which tends to let up with the coming of warm weather.

Doctor Levine gave eighteen angina pectoris sufferers injections of testosterone propionate, twenty-five milligrams three times a week *for four weeks,* and the length of time of treatment is important to remember. He continued the treatment in the case of one patient for seven weeks. The results in general were disappointing.

He based his judgment of results on the patient's own estimate of the amount of physical activity he was able to engage in without bringing on an attack of that rending heart pain, and by the number of nitroglycerine tablets that had to be used in twenty-four hours' time to stop the acute attacks, which is all that nitroglycerine can do, it not being in any sense a cure for angina pectoris.

Doctor Levine noted marked improvement after the testosterone injections in only five of those nineteen angina pectoris sufferers. But two of them reverted to their original condition within six to eight weeks; one was better for four months, and another for one month only. In eleven patients no change in their bouts of agony was produced by testosterone during this four weeks of treatment or at any time thereafter. It was Doctor Levine's overall conclusion that the improvement of these five sufferers really might mean nothing at all, because the pains of angina pectoris have a way of getting better for a while spontaneously.

Being myself prejudiced in favor of the pure male hormone, it irked me that in eleven of these nineteen patients it had shown no good effect at all. But, just the same, prejudice aside, Doctor Levine's experiments did stir up certain questions. In the first place, assuming for a moment that the easing of the pain in those five patients wasn't a happenstance but actually an effect of testosterone, then it was perfectly natural that they should relapse after the treatment was over. Because the most starry-eyed enthusiast would never claim that testosterone would *cure* angina pectoris or any other sad condition of older men. If it would do anything at all, it would only replace what the older men's testicles were no longer producing, and which, apparently, at least in these particular men, was essential to the proper functioning of the blood vessels that nourish the heart muscles.

In short, to get any long-continued killing of angina pectoris pain, to have any long-time strengthening action on the ailing heart, you'd have to go on giving testosterone indefinitely. Because, in older men, it would be folly to hope for a spontaneous comeback of male hormone production by their own testicles.

It did bother me a bit, though, that in the case of one patient benefited, and then relapsing, a second course of testosterone treatment failed to kill the pain.

But here was a more serious question about Doctor Levine's experiments. Had he gone on long enough with the testosterone treatment with the eleven patients in whom he failed and in the one who failed after the second course of injections? Four weeks' treatment in all. . . . Was that enough to strengthen the muscles of those ailing hearts or to widen their narrowed blood vessels?

Doctor Levine himself had the scientific integrity to say that a number of other physicians had tested the effect of the male hormone upon angina pectoris and that *"the results so far had been uniformly favorable."* He didn't try to belittle the success of the other doctors; he didn't try to do a dirty on testosterone by not mentioning the names and publications of physicians who thought it was powerful against angina pectoris. No scientific snide was our Doctor Levine. He simply reported his own negative results for what they were worth, and that was that.

At about this same time in the early nineteen-forties another Boston doctor, Maurice A. Lesser, was trying out testosterone in an effort to relieve the terrible heart pain of angina pectoris. Now it is true that Doctor Lesser could not compete with Doctor Levine's distinction of being on the medical faculty of Harvard University. Just the same, Doctor Lesser was Instructor in preventive medicine at the Boston University School of Medicine and visiting physician to the Massachusetts Memorial Hospitals.

You could not call him a medical outcast.

Despite Doctor Lesser's more humble rank in the medical hierarchy his trial of testosterone seemed to me to be pretty careful and even hard-boiled. He might be criticized from one angle: he began testing the male hormone's effect upon angina pectoris in June when, you remember, the disease tends to be milder than it is in Winter.

Just the same, he was tough enough on testosterone to try it out on people with severe angina pectoris. His patients were twenty men and four women, from forty to seventy-seven years old; all had bad pain over their hearts or under their breastbones, brought on by emotion or exertion; and in all of them, that pain was temporarily eased by nitroglycerine—which purely temporarily widens the arteries of the heart. All of these twenty-four victims had at least one attack daily and most of them, several. And here was good news—

Most of them, said Doctor Lesser, were treated during the Fall and Winter when their disease was at its most severe. That took at least one bug out of his experiment.

All of them improved under the testosterone injections, but the men reported an easing of their pain that was much more striking than that of the women. And to make sure that this effect wasn't fooling him with that old scientific malarkey known as suggestion, Doctor Lesser, without the patients themselves knowing it, gave five of them a series of six blank injections, containing nothing but sterile oil. No testosterone.

None of these so-called control human experimental animals showed any easing of their pain following these blank injections, in marked contrast to the general improvement that Doctor Lesser noted in patients treated with testosterone propionate.

And when he switched those control patients (without their knowing it) to the real testosterone, they began getting better; they could exert themselves physically more and more, with less and less attacks of that agony over their hearts and with less severity of the attacks when they did happen.

Doctor Lesser was scientifically tough in another way, in the kind of tests to which he put his treated angina pectoris victims. After the good results on his first twenty-four people, he wasn't satisfied and did the whole experiment over on twenty-two more. He wasn't satisfied with simply asking them whether they could exert themselves more, with less frequent pain after the testosterone injections. That was too vague. So he put a certain number of this second series of patients to what's called an exercise tolerance test. It was the so-called "two-step" test that gives a definite measure of the severity of heart disease. It was designed by Doctors A. M. Master and E. T. Oppenheimer, and the point was, you could put it in figures.

Under Doctor Lesser's direct personal observation, these human heart-threatened guinea-pigs walked up one side of a little two-step stairs and walked down the other and then turned right around and did that over and over, solemnly; it seemed idiotic until suddenly, bang, their faces contorted and they broke out in a sweat with that horrible pain under their breastbones or over their hearts. This test made it quantitative, scientific, measurable. You could pretty closely determine the amount of exertion that brought on the heart attack in a given person.

Doctor Lesser put his patients through this little two-step test agony again and again before he treated them with testosterone—"to obtain a base-line for comparison," he said, coldly, regarding their condition before testosterone treatment and after.

In each of the patients put through this deliberate ordeal the amount of work they could do was strikingly increased before they'd develop an anginal attack. It was a pretty accurate measure of testosterone's action. And when the pains did come, they were not as terrible and did not last so long. And the pain-easing power of testosterone meant more than the seemingly silly academic triumph of making the patients climb up and down those little steps, let's say, a hundred times instead of thirty times before they were stopped cold by that awful pain. The power of testosterone reached into their lives as productive citizens.

A fifty-year-old boilermaker had a history of angina pectoris that had lasted nine months, that was getting worse and worse, so that for the past four months he couldn't work at all and was definitely on the shelf as a heart invalid. The electrocardiogram test suggested he'd had a blood clot that had blocked a heart artery. His heart muscle was starved for blood. After six injections of testosterone propionate, the ex-boilermaker could make eighty trips up and down those stairs, instead of forty, before the heart pains hit him.

Now this man returned to his work as a boilermaker; and at the time of this writing, he'd experienced no more attacks.

Digging more closely into Doctor Lesser's strict observation of the effect of testosterone upon his patients, I found a possible hint of a reason why he had succeeded where Doctor Levine had failed. "The improvement," said Doctor Lesser, "after the use of this drug (testosterone) varies with the individual patient both in time of onset and in degree."

Some of the heart victims began to notice fewer and shorter blizzards of pain in their hearts after two or three injections of the male hormone. Some not till twelve injections had gone by, at the rate of three shots a week. Some were discouraged, continuing to live under this pain that's like the hand of death grabbing your heart, till fifteen and even twenty-five injections had been made; only then did it feel to them as if that hand of death was growing lighter.

Striking an average among his forty-six patients for the time their improvement began, Doctor Lesser said it was on the average twenty-eight days before quantitative, measurable improvement could be noted at all and forty-three days before that betterment became marked.

Twenty-eight to forty-three days? Well, well! This, on the average, *was longer than the time Doctor Levine had continued his testosterone injections.*

It would be maybe more accurate to say then that testosterone had no effect on the pain of angina pectoris when its injections were continued for one month.

Medically, Doctor Lesser was no village idiot. He knew that improvement, temporary, spontaneous, and due to no treatment at all, may occur in some angina pectoris patients over weeks and months. The agony does have mysterious let-ups and ups and downs. But what hit him about these forty-six sufferers was that testosterone had knocked out the heart pains of so many people so uniformly in such a short space of time.

Of course it was very pleasant to be the human guinea-pig in such a successful experiment as this one, but how long would the blasting agony stay away from your chest after the test was over, after the end of the injections? Doctor Lesser said his experiment hadn't gone on long enough for him to say. He promised his patients nothing. He could only say that some stayed free of heart pain for two months. One patient hadn't felt a twinge for eighteen months. That was the Exhibit A, so far. It was a bit encouraging, though, that when the patients did relapse and came back begging for the shots of testosterone, they said their new pain wasn't as bad as before those first injections.

It seemed that it took fewer injections of testosterone to bring these relapsers under control again.

Here, so far, I could take my choice between Doctor Levine, negative, and Doctor Lesser, positive, about the power of testosterone over the grave heart symptoms of angina pectoris. Now studying further, the weight of evidence seemed to tilt the scale toward Lesser's good news. Doctor L. Hamm, also of Boston, agreed that the pure male hormone had this pain-killing power. Among seven angina pectoris cases, from fifty-two to seventy-five years old, testosterone injected three times a week for from six to eight weeks, and then once a month, brought easing of their heart pain in all of them and no return of it even after walking several city blocks and climbing two or three flights of stairs. And, mind you, they were all tough cases, most of them carrying their nitroglycerine tablets along with them constantly.

What also excited Doctor Hamm was what physicians call a side-effect of testosterone. Only they usually use this term in the bad sense, but here the side-effects were the opposite and remarkable. The skin of these people changed from sallow to pink, gradually; and all of them showed an up of mental as well as physical endurance and agility. They insisted they felt better and better. It was that bad condition the doctors call euphoria. Why it's bad I do not know, excepting that maybe it is not decent to feel euphoric after you've passed the age of fifty. It is not what God intended.

Doctor Hamm took a polite swipe at carping medical critics who'd say this erasing of pain of his patients was merely subjective, no evidence. "The special nature of the symptoms of angina pectoris," said Doctor Hamm, "allows them to be viewed in an objective light."

Had these carpers ever had an attack themselves?

"The pain . . . is classic in intensity, and the most stoic patient gives creditable information when he says he did or did not have this pain," said Hamm.

Now the scales weighed heavier on the side of testosterone's heart-easing power. Doctor Taylor C. Walker of Beaumont, Texas, reported that though his results were not so uniformly favorable as those of Doctors Lesser and Hamm, still seven out of nine patients with real angina pectoris improved after a series of injections of testosterone propionate. And from the very respectable medical school of the Ohio State University (though it is not to be mentioned in the same breath with Harvard, of course) Doctors R. W. Bonnell, C. P. Pritchett, and T. E. Rardin reported a four-year test of sex hormone treatment of twenty-three heart-stricken angina pectoris patients, carefully diagnosed, all of them coming under Classes II, III, and IV—in an ascending order of severity—according to the criteria of heart trouble as established by the august American Heart Association.

The Ohio doctors treated these people with both female and male sex hormones; and they'd begun before testosterone was available, way back in 1936; and for a male hormone they'd used a urine concentrate of impure androsterone, which was testosterone's waste product and not nearly so powerful.

Twenty-two out of twenty-three of these tortured people showed improvement during the hormone treatment—six, complete relief, five, excellent relief but occasional mild pains, and eleven, what could be called a good result though they still experienced occasional mild heart attacks.

Now I began to look at the sad side of this hopeful science. I couldn't help being reminded of Doctor Guy Laroche's seven sad old Frenchmen. What would be the fate of these heart-stricken people that the American doctors had given new life, new hope? Out of Doctor Lesser's original twenty-four angina pectoris patients, four had died a year, six months, four months *after the testosterone treatment had been discontinued.*

One had died of a coronary occlusion two-and-a-half months after the testosterone treatment had begun, though his pain had been eased notably.

Now I asked myself, What if the testosterone treatment had been continued, had gone on indefinitely, the way you treat diabetics with insulin? If a hormone hunger was a factor in the starving of the heart for blood, it was absolutely wrong to expect a limited number of injections to satisfy that hunger, permanently.

I thought bitterly of the more than one hundred thousand annual deaths (over and beyond those from rheumatic heart disease in the earlier stages of life) that hit Americans, stricken with heart disease in life's afternoon and evening. Till now, aside from the momentary relief of such pain-killers as nitroglycerine, the best the greatest heart specialist could do for many of these hundreds of thousands of angina pectoris patients was to tell them to take it easy.

Now here was testosterone, apparently striking more fundamentally at heartbreak maybe widening the heart's arteries so that the heart muscle would be less starved for blood, maybe strengthening those muscles themselves by giving them more glycogen that's the fuel for the heart's energy.

Now I pondered about the aim and purpose in life of many of the heart specialists of America. Was it simply to become very expert in the diagnosis of our heartsick hundreds of thousands of older people? Was it simply to give them bottles of nitroglycerine or aminophylline and to pat them on the back and to tell them to take it easy? Were those Boston, Columbus, and Texas doctors liars about testosterone? Were they fooling themselves? Were they quacks in their claims about the male hormone? Biologically, scientifically, testosterone was a body-builder, synthesizing protein, building muscle. It was more than a possible revigorator of sexually ambitious and rather nasty old men. After their horrible pain had been eased, after a new energy and new hope had been made to upsurge in these stricken people, why then had the testosterone been discontinued?

Was it because the pure male hormone was too expensive

to be given indefinitely? That was likely one angle. If so, what was the money value of a man on the shady side of life's afternoon?

This is not to say that testosterone had already been proved to prolong the life of a single heart-stricken man. But if the terrible heart pain of angina pectoris was in general a symptom of the starvation of the heart for blood, and if that pain was relieved for a long time by testosterone in many people, then mightn't it be that testosterone was *beginning* to give their hearts a new lease on life?

What was needed to answer these grave questions was perfectly obvious. Namely, a long-time test, upon a large number of patients definitely diagnosed by expert heart specialists to be suffering from unquestioned heart disease, a trial extending over many years, to answer yes or no, whether testosterone could actually prolong their lives.

Could our leading heart specialists, who are men of the highest medical dignity, break through a possible prejudice against testosterone because of its unfortunate sexual origin? And if they could do so, what was against their setting up such a human experiment, not for a couple of years but to extend over a generation?

Medical defeatists might object that it might not be safe to give testosterone for five or ten years or twenty. And might not the human body set up a tolerance against its action, so that its effect would wear off? The only answer is that you wouldn't know till you tried it. The distinguished endocrinologist, Doctor Joseph Eidelsberg, of New York City, reports that large amounts of testosterone can be given continuously over periods of years to eunuchoid almost-men, without any harm to them and without any loss of the wonderful new manhood that testosterone has given them.

CHAPTER TWENTY-ONE

THERE I go jumping the gun again. Here I am, agitating at our leading heart specialists to get going on such a long-time experiment while the first hopeful hints (and you can't call them more than hints) of testosterone's heart-building power are hot off the press. Give the boys time, brother, give the boys time. Remember that what's happened so far is nothing spectacular. It's nothing like insulin's bringing comatose diabetics back from the grave. I'll say it isn't. Why don't I remember that this angina pectoris belongs in the class of those inevitable degenerative breakdowns from which most men are *supposed* to die after fifty or sixty or seventy? I should remember not to be too damned theoretical and scientific. I can hear the big heart specialists giving me the horse laugh. What if testosterone does build the voluntary muscles of men as well as guinea-pigs, it doesn't follow from this that testosterone will strengthen the *in*voluntary muscles of the human heart. What if the male hormone does put good glycogen fuel into the hearts of rats, and what if it does increase the size of the hearts of castrated rats; that doesn't mean it'll do the same for the hearts of men. What if the hormones, male and female, do widen the experimentally spasmed arteries of the tails of rats and even the spasmed arteries of the legs and feet of women and men, does it follow that the male hormone will relax and widen the arteries so they'll bring more good blood to the ailing human heart?

I can hear the assembled heart specialists giving me the Bronx cheer. Remember, brother, that the clinical experience with testosterone against aging hearts is still feeble. Who, after all, *are* those fellows from Boston, Columbus and, of all the tank-town medical places, Beaumont, Texas, who now claim testosterone really kills angina pectoris pain? Do they rate as cardiologists? I don't know. And what was the result of this treatment when an authoritative heart man, Doctor Levine from Harvard, tried it? Negative!

So I say to myself, "Let's forget the project of trying to find out whether testosterone can actually prolong the lives of victims of angina pectoris. Let's call it a day."

Then I remember Herman Bundesen and Pat O'Brien. Then I take a hitch in my belt and go back at it. I ask the heart specialists: Who was Banting before he discovered insulin? Who was Manfred Sakel before he began shocking schizophrenics back to sanity? They were nobodies. What "authority" ever discovered anything? Not one. They're too busy politicking themselves into becoming authorities.

Let's try to get somebody to start this long-time project to see if testosterone will keep these heart victims alive. Keep up your courage, brother! The cost of testosterone is going down. Now it can be taken by mouth, conveniently and safely so that the poor devils won't have to come back and stand in line in a dingy charity clinic three times a week for shots of it in their arms or behinds. Let's look for a couple of young medical stronghearts, young Herman Bundesens and Pat O'Briens, optimists, not defeatists, who'd have the guts to get this unorthodox heart fight going.

They might, you know, if they could get a big grant of money to buy the testosterone for years and to pay the salaries of the clinicians and medical follow-up workers for years. But where is the money to come from for such a long-odds scientific gamble? From nowhere. Don't fool yourself, brother. The Government, or any big foundation, or any rich man who might have the money necessary for finding out if testosterone, by mending hearts, could actually extend the life span, all of them would go right away to the big shots of the American Heart Association.

So lay off it, brother. Take it easy. Don't worry about them dying. Go on trusting Herman Bundesen and Pat O'Brien and above all, go on trusting the basic science of testosterone, the builder. Go on taking your own methyl testosterone every day. Maybe, who knows, it may help keep your own heart arteries open and strengthen your own heart muscle. What are you writing this story of testosterone for, anyway? To save the world? No, you've dug into this science only to find out if Herman Bundesen is right about testosterone maybe chemically renewing your own worn-out human soil. So far the evidence is on the side of Herman, even if the medical authorities, the big shots, smile at it. So just don't forget to take your twenty or thirty milligrams of methyl testosterone a day. Maybe, who knows, it'll help you to live to laugh at them.

Maybe there are some other good chemical tricks that testosterone can do upon my aging body. In my late forties and early fifties I faced it that I was slowing down, mentally. The old humor was dying. I was beginning to take the world seriously. I began to forget that I was really only a reporter and started to try to help improve the world instead of sticking to my job of trying to tell what a funny and sad and interesting show human life really is. Now I'd been taking methyl testosterone for a year, and with due regard and respect for all the world's tragedy, I could begin to laugh again; and I'd become clear-headed enough to realize that I'd been a flop as a public health agitator and do-gooder and that I should stick to my job as a plain reporter. Had the testosterone helped me?

Maybe wasn't there another strength hiding in those little white pills besides their possible strength for my muscles and heart? What was the effect of testosterone on the mental disease of aging men?

CHAPTER TWENTY-TWO

So I went back to the fundamentals, back to testosterone's weird power over the mental and spiritual lives of the eunuchoid almost-men and the castrated broken men. I remembered how Doctor James B. Hamilton and his helpers were amazed at the new male hormone's effect upon those men's brains. As they got new manhood they'd never had or regained a manhood they'd lost, their despond changed to elation. They were all less broken in spirit. They became aggressive. They grew more strong-thinking and less sissified. They lost their irritability and sullen brooding and no longer broke into fits of whimpering. They were more stable and had self-control. Their intense mental fatigue vanished and was replaced by mental energy and stamina. For all of them, hope took the place of their old despair.

Now in men in mid-life and in life's evening there is without question a waning in their natural production of testosterone; and in some men at this time of life, there is a mental breakdown known as involutional melancholia, the crazy sadness of the folding-up phase of living. Such sufferers are to be found in all of our asylums, and outside of them too, guarded by their families who are ashamed. They are confused and forgetful and often mute. They may hear nonexistent voices and see crazy visions. They accuse themselves of crimes they've never committed. They may believe the world's against them and their despond often leads them to suicide.

Could some of these cases of involutional melancholia be

laid to a male hormone hunger? The male hormone's miraculous restoration of the mental state of those castrated broken men gave hormone-hunting physicians a clue, gave them at least fairly sound scientific reason for trying testosterone. They had another fact to encourage them: among women at the time of their change of life, the new pure female hormones, when they were given in big enough doses and persistently and skilfully, were lifting many such women out of their crazy sorrow.

Before the end of the nineteen-thirties, reports of the power of testosterone against mysterious mid-life madness of men began to come from Germany—in 1937 from Doctor Gisbert Schmitz in Berlin and in 1939 from Doctor O. L. Weiss in Bonn. But these Germans gave no careful scientific details. And then too the good effects—like those of Doctor Heinz Arndt, you remember—were too universal. I had no way of finding out whether Doctors Schmitz and Weiss were scientific observers or Nazi doctors.

But nothing is more deeply significant in the fight for life than the resurrection, physical or mental, of a human being who by the judgment of a hard-boiled doctor is surely doomed. And this was without question the condition of a seventy-four-year-old wreck of a man who was admitted to Bailbrook House, in Bath, in England. The curious events now happening in the case of this doomed man were reported, in 1940, in the *British Medical Journal*, by the medical superintendent of Bailbrook House, Doctor Arthur Guirdham.

This seventy-four-year-old being that you could no longer call a man was suffering acute melancholia. He was convinced he was financially ruined. He asserted that there was a blocking of passage of food from his mouth to his stomach. By his bedside he insisted on keeping a can into which he spat incessantly. (He said he was spitting out food that could not pass into his stomach.) He had sugar in his urine, resulting from chronic inflammation of his pancreas. He had extreme degeneration of the blood vessels, including those of his heart. The blocking of the arteries in his feet was so severe that a specialist, called in, said there was immediate danger of gangrene.

He was a human vestige.

What could you do for him? Nothing. So Doctor Guirdham began giving him shots of testosterone propionate, small doses, only five milligrams, one every fourth day till he'd given twelve injections in all.

"At the end of this," said Doctor Guirdham, "he seemed better physically and more cheerful and alert mentally."

But the change in the old man was not enough to impress Doctor Guirdham. Except in one particular. It was clear that the blood was beginning to run strong in the arteries of the old man's feet again. They got back a healthier color. The danger of that impending gangrene seemed definitely over.

Then three and a half months later, Doctor Guirdham put the man on a course of male hormone, much weaker than testosterone, the waste product of testosterone that's excreted in the urine. It was what chemist Butenandt first got out in that whisper of crystals, a few milligrams of crystals from twenty-five thousand liters of human urine. It was called androsterone, now known to be a waste product of testosterone, slightly chemically different, yet having the same hormone action, only not so strong. Doctor Guirdham now put the poor old duffer on a course of little shots of this weaker male hormone, one every fourth day, for twelve shots in all. Now slowly he became definitely more cheerful and began to think of other things than the imaginary food that wouldn't go from his mouth to his stomach.

"One hesitated to exaggerate," said Doctor Guirdham, "what might have been no more than a transient improvement in, to all intents and purposes, a hopeless illness."

He kept waiting for the old man to go crazy again, or to check out with a stroke or heart failure. "But after a month," said Doctor Guirdham, "this improvement was unmistakable."

For three and a half months he went on improving solidly and steadily and gained more than seven pounds and had insight into how idiotic he'd been about his financial ruin and the blockage of his gullet. "I was out of my head when I thought such rot," you can imagine this resurrected old man saying, smiling.

He left the hospital. Some weeks later the old man's wife informed Doctor Guirdham that the depression was all gone, that his improvement was amazing, and that he was able to sing duets with his daughter.

Doctor Guirdham could not trace this return of the old man from the shadows to anything else but the courses of testosterone and androsterone.

"The vast majority of psychiatrists would agree," said Doctor Guirdham, "that anything other than the most inconsiderable alleviation of symptoms, except the superficial pseudo-improvement associated with the blurred outlines of a supervening dementia, could not be expected of a case of melancholia with delusions . . . in a grossly arteriosclerotic old man seventy-four years of age."

What Guirdham meant was that most psychiatrists would consider this a miracle.

What impressed him was that neither this old man nor two other younger insane men who recovered as a result of male hormone injections, had any outward sign of sex gland deficiency. What stirred him was the strange wallop these hormones had, now that they were crystal pure.

"I, myself, have experimented before with glandular extracts of the most divergent nature," said Doctor Guirdham, "alike only in the extravagance of the claims made for them and in their uniform uselessness."

But he was quite convinced, he said, that these pure hormone products were of a potency not heretofore encountered. "It may well be that in this direction lies a future hope in the treatment of psychotic conditions," he concluded.

Now quickly came news from hospitals and mental disease institutions, making it seem as if Doctor Guirdham's hopes for the male hormones were far from foolish. At the Springfield State Hospital at Sykesville, Maryland, there were two psychiatrists of the modern type (still not too common) who believed they should try to be something more than mere keepers of more or less hopeless inmates of insane asylums. They believed that mental disease is chemical. Their names were Doctor Lewis Danziger and Doctor H. Robert Blank and now they began shooting testosterone propionate into a little series of five cases of agitated depression in men aged fifty and over. They were all more or less arteriosclerotic. They were diagnosed by the staff to be suffering that sadness of the folding-up phase of life, involutional melancholia.

They ruled out the possibility that the shots were working as mere suggestion by beginning with injections of salt solution—no testosterone. Then they began injecting the male hormone, three times a week, twenty-five milligrams of testosterone propionate.

What now happened to a man, sixty-nine years old, amazed them. He was confused, sleepless, mute, and forgetful. He was depressed, agitated, resistant, delusional, and had hallucinations. He mumbled about people being tortured, starved, and killed. He wouldn't eat, mumbling other folks needed food more than he did, and he was undernourished, weak, and had trembling hands. For a month the doctors gave this old wreck those mock injections—nothing doing.

After the fifth injection of testosterone propionate he began coming out of the dark of his hopeless madness. He began to gain weight and eat, and he became cheerful. He became calm. After the twelfth shot of testosterone he could be called gay, for an old man; and he had fully recovered mentally.

After six weeks of treatment, this sixty-nine-year-old man announced with great pleasure the return of sexual desire and powerful erections.

His improvement was maintained at the time Doctors Danziger and Blank published their paper. Three out of the five cases treated with testosterone came rapidly out of their mental shadow; and upon the other two, testosterone had no result. They admitted their number of cases was too small to be statistically significant, but they were sure that in those three far-gone mentally sick men, testosterone acted like a specific; and the treatment was encouraging enough to justify further trials.

Now from other institutions came reports that testosterone was like a chemical key opening a chemical lock in mentally diseased people past middle life, not in all of them, mind you, but with the power of the pure male hormone you could get a quick yes or no to the question of whether their sickness was a hormone hunger.

Besides that Englishman, Arthur Guirdham, six other groups of American investigators reported success against this middle and later life madness by treatment with testosterone. They'd treated thirty patients in all, with complete recovery or marked improvement in twenty-one of them, and temporary improvement in four more. This unanimity was contradicted only by Doctor H. A. Barahal, who treated five patients with testosterone and reported that it had no effect upon their involutional melancholia.

Of course those five may not have been suffering from male hormone hunger. The next five, if Doctor Barahal had gone on trying, might have snapped out of their dementias, who knows? Doctors Eugene Davidoff and Gerald Goodstone, of Syracuse, New York, kept trying the pure male hormone on demented, melancholic, middle-aged and older men till they'd got a series of twenty of them. And thirteen of the twenty responded well to testosterone. The Syracuse doctors didn't for a moment maintain that the male hormone was a panacea for mental disease; and they reported that mild and moderately severe involutional melancholia responded much better than the severe type among whom only two out of seven patients were slightly improved. They warned that in the severe type of this crazy sadness, testosterone was dangerous, might be dynamite. During treatment, one patient became more agitated and tried suicide and another went into the tailspin of a vasomotor collapse.

Yet they were conservatively sanguine about it. They proposed psychiatrists might use the male hormone as a rapid therapeutic test to find out how much of this involutional insanity might actually be due to male hormone hunger.

They *might* take thousands out of our jam-packed asylums!

If testosterone could take men who were actually psychotic with involutional melancholia out of insane asylums, what mightn't be its power to *prevent* this madness? What might it do to sharpen the wits and boost the mental energy and raise the optimism of numberless men who drift into fits of despond, who feel they are finished in those bad years past fifty?

To you and to me, to us fuddy-duddies past fifty these are real questions. In a mass sense, to the nation, to increase its productive brain power, these questions are still silly. There is not a single public health organization, local, state, or national, that's equipped to even start to find out whether the male hormone can prolong life's prime and raise our total vitality.

PART V

A NEW LEASE ON LIFE

This is the morning of the first big 1944 snow, and Wake Robin is cut off from the world, snowbound; and I feel very alone with my responsibility. This morning I'm a bit upset about my hero, even though that hero is no human being at all but only the keto-steroid chemical known as testosterone. My chemical hero has climbed from success to success and still he is sniggered about and smiled at contemptuously by many doctors, and I begin to worry and wonder where it all will end. I've tried to be accurate. I don't want to draw a long bow and tell it bigger than it really is. I have regard and even reverence for testosterone's reputation, much more than for that of any merely fictional hero I could create, because deep down I feel what testosterone is doing for my present strength and my possible future. But I must be careful not to make testosterone out to be a chemical Horatio Alger boy, yet that's what its history has been. Testosterone started out as a laughed-at chemical, worth more than its weight in gold, yet nobody wanting it—and now it's getting cheaper and cheaper, but with doctors and laymen clamoring for it more and more so that it will make its producers wealthy.

Yes, it's a sort of scientific Horatio Alger yarn, this vital chemical's rise from the rags of its original sexual disreputability to the riches of its present promise of dominion over the total vitality of aging men.

There are parts of this story that have been tougher than any I've ever had to tell, because, unlike microbes, you can't make people *see* the structure in space of that organic chemical molecule, the steroid chemical of which testosterone is such a brilliant and promising chemical child. You can't make people understand the inspired ingenuity of those organic chemists, cooking and stewing and extracting and crystallizing till they got testosterone out pure and plentiful. It's hard to explain what a tough time testosterone had getting believed in at all, because it was discovered in the testicles in such foolishly, incredibly infinitesimal amounts. It's continually made in those tiny traces and not stored up at all, just as if it were meant never to be discovered and always to remain the most secret quintessence of life. It is as if God wished to hide testosterone from the curiosity of questing men who, if they found it, might be bold to use it to make mankind happier than God intended. It was good old Fred Koch who turned that tough scientific corner, and it is too bad that he was not included in the Nobel Prize along with Ružička and Butenandt.

When I began digging into testosterone's scientific history, I was not bothered about the fate of my chemical hero. It was really amusing to be able to tell how testosterone, when synthesized pure at last, began to bring manhood back to broken men and to make men of sad twenty-five-year-old boys who had never known manhood at all.

Then I thought it was a very fine story—to surprise you readers by the way the shame of testosterone's primary sexuality was wiped out, clean forgotten, by the accumulating observations that its vital force went far beyond that of turning a few eunuchoids into men who could enjoy the fun of mating. It was more than a writing trick; it was scientifically true.

But now the final fate of my hero, testosterone, really begins to bother me. It is deeply disturbing to discover how high is the chemical dignity of this originally raffish hero. Testosterone is actually one of the primary, the key, the master chemicals dominating the machinery of the bodies of men. Authoritative doctors may scoff at this. But will the plain citizens, the men past fifty, the ordinary readers believe it? It seems too good to be true. The news seems too good how testosterone hardens flabby muscles and makes muscles swell and be strong to work long without tiring. The news seems incredible how testosterone sharpens nerve reflexes and upsurges the mental power of the brain. What is most significant in the biological sense is that testosterone engineers the human body's building of its own proteins which are the stuff of life itself. Testosterone is the boy hero putting his thumb in the hole of the dike against those proteins' disintegration.

These deep powers might all be well and good and of limited importance if my hero, testosterone, had confined them merely to the rescue of those unfortunate almost-men and broken men, the eunuchoids who are, after all, a forgotten and negligible part of humanity. But here's what shakes me: this having to tell that the magic of testosterone might extend to normal men, with testicles, but physically and mentally tired and prematurely old.

This simply scares me. This smacks of rejuvenation. This can't be so. This gives me a bad case of buck fever. It pulls my writing wallop. I can't let myself go. To be honest, I doubt my hero, testosterone, the rebuilder.

That is my mood this snowy morning.

I actually began holding back and soft-pedalling other scientific facts, suggesting other astounding rebuilding virtues of testosterone. I sabotaged my hero. Well, let's out with those new facts now. I must admit now that hormone hunters V. Korenchevsky and M. A. Ross in London and Hans Selye in Montreal have discovered that the male hormone can increase the size of the cells of the kidneys of animals, and maybe the kidneys' functional action. This science has not yet been applied, so far as I know, to old human kidneys that are ailing. But what testosterone has been found to do for animals, it has almost always later been found to do for hormone-hungry men. So again, maybe, here was another example of testosterone, the rebuilder.

That scared me again. Too much like an elixir.

But now at last I'm flabbergasted by the hint of another and more ultimate force of this already too, too magic chemical. There had, so far, been one fundamental fact that had put a limit to its power. No matter what magic renewal the male hormone might accomplish in muscles, kidneys, nerves, and brain cells, after all, so what? A man's as old as his arteries! And those arteries deteriorate, sooner or later, but always inevitably. So no matter how much testosterone you do shoot into aging men, don't worry about extending their prime, because the vital parts that testosterone is boosting will eventually be starved for blood.

So testosterone will then be a mockery. The blood won't be able to get at those vital parts to nourish them when the blood vessels become blocked by vasomotor spasms, or by arteriosclerotic changes or by both. But here comes news that testosterone may have a controlling chemical action upon the vasomotor nerves. These are the sympathetic nerves that control the narrowing and widening of the little arteries that nourish the vital tissues of the body.

Here's the way it all started. Here's what the excellent surgeon, Doctor Louis G. Herrmann and his co-worker, Doctor Edward J. McGrath, of Cincinnati University, have just reported after ten years of observation upon the deteriorating blood vessels of the hands and legs and feet of hundreds of pain-racked and gangrenous women and men who were suffering from various forms of obliterative disease of the arteries and veins of the upper and lower limbs.

"In the majority of early and moderately advanced degenerative arterial disease," they've just written in the *American*

Journal of Surgery, "the influence of the vasomotor (nervous) mechanism is far from negligible."

They state that this is not merely their own opinion but that it has been corroborated by other clinical investigators. They mean that if you could do something chemically good for those vasomotor nerves, you might check, or even throw into reverse, to some degree, the fatal degeneration of the little arteries, those blood vessels upon which the integrity of life depends.

Now we'll have to leave Louis Herrmann and Edward McGrath for a moment and flash back to the early gropings of hormone hunter, James B. Hamilton, the anatomist, you remember, who was one of the very first to use testosterone to bring manhood to eunuchoid almost- and broken men. It is the luck of Hamilton that he was not a doctor but only a Ph.D. and that he was basically always like a hound on the scent of fundamental biologic powers of this new testosterone. One of the very first actions of the male hormone that he observed was its curious power to get good red blood to flowing in the pale, pasty, gray, withered skin of the heads, the hands, and the feet of the castrates, the broken men.

Then James Hamilton took a bold jump from those broken men to try the same possible effect of testosterone upon the deteriorated arteries of certain normal men, that is, men with normal-seeming testicles, but men with horrible pains in the calves of their legs and ulcers on their toes that portended the coming of dangerous gangrene. Not being an M.D., he had no right to treat them, so he called in Doctor Edward A. Edwards of Tufts College Medical School to make his experiment legal. Not being a physicist, Hamilton called in Mr. S. Quimby Duntley of the Massachusetts Institute of Technology, with gadgets that would measure precisely whether more blood was flowing in the blocked arteries of the skin of the feet and legs of these disabled and pain-racked people.

So now our hormone-hunting-medical-physical team proceeded to shoot testosterone propionate into seven human wrecks with obliterative degenerative arterial disease of their legs and feet. Some had frightful pain in their calf muscles after short walking—intermittent claudication. Some even had devastating cramps in their leg muscles while quiet in bed at night. Others had ulcers on their feet, prophesying the coming of dreaded gangrene.

Duntley's gadget, the spectro-photometer, quickly showed new good red blood running in the arteries, so that you could measure it, quantitatively. After testosterone.

And Doctors Edwards and Hamilton? They could feel the pulsing of arteries coming back again in pulseless legs and feet; and they watched the healing of the dangerous ulcers. After testosterone.

And the patients? They could walk much further without their calf muscles cramping, and they no longer had cramps at night in bed and in some of them, under testosterone, the pain faded completely.

And under the gentle power of testosterone they felt something no gadget could measure. They felt an upsurge of energy and a feeling of hooray for tomorrow.

Did testosterone, then, really check arterial degeneration? For a while I've had a nasty sabotaging feeling of satisfaction that this hope of testosterone for these seven crippled men might be only one of those things, a scientific howler. Two other groups of workers have failed to confirm this success of testosterone that held out such promise to hundreds of thousands of men who are in pain and disabled in our country because their feet and leg arteries are deteriorating.* And it would seem a cozier and more modest and less

* Doctor Herman Zurrow and his co-workers, and also Doctors Samuel Beaser and Theodore Massell, are unable to confirm this particular power cf testosterone. On the other hand, other groups of hormone hunters do corroborate the observation of Doctor Hamilton and his associates.

far-reaching adventure if testosterone had no power to check the degeneration of arteries.

But now it is necessary to flash forward again to Louis Herrmann and Edward McGrath. Their ten years of experience bring a hint that Hamilton's hunch was right. For ten years McGrath and Herrmann had been experimenting with the power, not of testosterone, but of the *female* hormones to check arterial degeneration.

They shot the female hormones, estrone and then estradiol dipropionate, into three hundred and forty-five women and men with arterial degenerative disease of their hands and feet and legs. They ruled out all cases in which the blood vessel disease was purely arteriosclerotic, was purely a thickening of the blood vessel walls, and in whom there was no chance of those vasomotor nerves, controlling the blood vessels, being out of whack or not working at all.

At the end of that ten years they now reported, in their low-keyed scientific way, that the results of this female hormone treatment were "satisfactory" in three hundred and thirty out of three hundred and forty-five pain-racked disabled women and men in the middle years of life! What those men and women called these results I do not know, but they did feel blood running through their hands and legs and feet again, and they felt a new warmth and new life in them, and an easing of their awful cramps after short-distance walking, and the fading from their feet of the ulcers that were the menace of oncoming gangrene.

Now here is how McGrath and Herrmann's story bore upon Hamilton's results with testosterone. The female hormones, estrone and estradiol, *are chemical sisters of the male hormone, testosterone.*

What the female hormone did was to release the chemical, acetyl-choline, from the ends of the vasomotor nerves that control the little arteries, so that the little arteries widen, so that good blood flows through them to the tissues. And

now, when, excited and disturbed, I long-distance-tele-
phoned Louis Herrmann, bothered by the failure of those
other searchers to confirm what Hamilton had found about
testosterone's power to check deterioration of arteries, Louis
was calmly reassuring.

"Testosterone ought to work just as well," said Louis.
"You know how testosterone and estradiol work in parallel,
testosterone in men and estradiol in women. You know how
they're chemically related," he said.

Now I had to face it. Could it be that this strengthening
of the action of the nerves controlling the little arteries of
the heart and the brain, could it be that this explained testosterone's power to ease the pain of heart-wrecked men, and
to bring back mental clearness to the sick brains of men crazy
with involutional melancholia?

This was no idea of mine, you understand, but it was the
belief of Doctors Bonnell, Pritchett, and Rardin who had
used both the male and female hormones to ease the pain of
so many of their patients in the agony of angina pectoris.
Banking on the fundamental significance of Louis Herrmann's and Edward McGrath's researches, those heart doctors believed that here was the clearing up of the riddle of
how the sex hormones made some sick hearts stronger. By
widening the little arteries that nourish the muscles of the
heart. By controlling the spasms of those little arteries.

But how could this help to explain how testosterone
cleared the addled brains of men crazy with involutional
melancholia? A curious little set of observations on the effect
of both the female and the male hormones upon certain old
and dying women and men gave a clue to this mental mystery. Doctor H. D. Cogswell of Whiting, Indiana, and
Doctor S. C. Davis, of Tucson, Arizona, together reported
their death-fighting teamwork in the *American Journal of
Surgery*.

It had struck them how many senile individuals have died

and are now dying "due to our lack of knowledge of the physiology of the aged." They were intrigued by a mortal mystery that most good surgeons have encountered. A senile person, after an accident often trivial, is placed in bed to recover, but instead breaks down mentally or physically and dies.

The course of these lethal events is strange. After being abed for a while, these battered old people become restless. They don't know what day it is or where they are. They become lethargic and often drift into a coma. They can't think straight. When they aren't in a coma, they often can't sleep and are very cantankerous. Then they die.

Doctor Cogswell and Doctor Davis took a whirl with the hormones at saving the life of two mildly banged-up old women and one not very badly hurt old man. Their theory was really simple and quaint. They gave them the hormones because such a mysterious craziness and dying is not ordinarily seen in younger people who have mild accidents, and the difference between younger and older people is simply (?) that the older ones are likely to be hungry for sex hormones!

It is illuminating and germane to our adventure to recount what they saw testosterone do for a dying old man. He was sixty-five and had been brought into the hospital following an automobile accident, not bad, abrasions and tenderness over both legs and in the small of his back. Okay, except that his heart was enlarged and his heart auricles were fibrillating and his blood pressure was 180/110—pretty high.

Then in two days he became confused in his mind. His talk made no sense at all. His memory had gone haywire. Couldn't even remember seeing the nurse who gave him his breakfast. His heart was fibrillating badly and pneumonia threatened in the bases of both of his lungs, and his abdomen was distended. It seemed it was going to be just another one of those things. Very mysterious. Just too bad. So they began giving him shots of testosterone propionate on their theory that this was what he was principally fundamentally short of. Twenty-five milligrams every three days, for just twelve days. He began clearing mentally within four days, and within fourteen days he was mentally sharp and feeling fine and was discharged from the hospital right side up and walking.

The state of two women, similarly mildly hurt, was still graver, really psychotic and going downhill fast; and again estrone, the female hormone, brought them back to sanity and back to life.

About this little string of miracles, our doctors, Cogswell and Davis, were cautious, conservative, and modest.

"Three cases are not enough from which to draw conclusions," they wrote, "but the results have been gratifying enough to warrant further investigation and trial."

In defense of their haste on getting into print, it may be here remarked that George Minot was set afire by what liver-feeding did to only a couple of cases of absolutely fatal pernicious anemia and Banting, ditto, by his first case of fatal diabetic coma that insulin pulled out of the grave; and that, if you waited to start to save lives till you had a statistically significant number of dying people, you might still be waiting for liver-feeding and insulin. Discovery, cutting, and trying, pioneering and probing life-saving experiment is *never* statistical.

What now fascinated me about these hormone experiments upon those crazy dying people was the explanation Doctor Cogswell and Doctor Davis made of how the male and female hormones acted to bring them back to mental strength and to vigorous life.

The walls, said the doctors, of the blood vessels of the brains of senile people are likely to be sclerotic, thickened, so that there's likely to be a borderline lack of oxygen in the brain tissue. The accidents, though trivial, are likely to cause a shock, and the result of such shock may be a stimulation of the vasomotor nerves so that they'll spasm and shut down the little arteries of the brain. So that the brain will be starved for blood.

As always, self-centered as I am, all this makes me woolgather now, gazing out over the pure white snow, through the woods, and out over Lake Michigan's steel gray water to the line of the horizon that this morning, with the barometer high, is sharp and clear like the line between life and death.

All these people, the heartwrecked, pain-racked victims of angina pectoris, the men gabbling idiotically and sad with involutional melancholia, the women and men cramped with the searing torture of pain in their blood-starved leg muscles; and these old women and this old man who were so mildly banged about, yet so mysteriously dying—all of them might be examples of what Herman Bundesen calls worn-out human soil.

All of them might be male or female hormone hungry.

Without any other treatment, the male and female hormones had eased their pain and cleared their brains and raised their total vitality, and even brought some of them back from the edge of the grave, to live again.

"Very well"—in the words of my friend, Curtis Gray, when he wishes, in his mentally precise manner, to sum up both sides of a debatable question and to put a period to garrulous and fruitless controversy—"very well, all doubters of the possible power of testosterone over total vitality, I bid you good day." For myself, daily and every day, so long as my pocketbook can stand it, I'll keep feeding the hormone hunger of my aging body with methyl testosterone. It may help a bit to keep my muscles, my nerves, my kidneys, and maybe even my little blood vessels in that reasonable state of vitality compatible with my general and obvious advancing senility.

Here I can gain courage from distinguished Doctor Louis I. Dublin. He says, "Some discoveries have been so extraordinary as to suggest that in the future, when more knowledge of the hormones . . . is obtained, powerful aids will be at our command to maintain healthy and vigorous bodies."

I'll start right now. I will try to renew my aging tissues with testosterone as long as I can, despite the contemptuous smiles or the laughter or the sneers of the ghosts of Doctor Warthin and Doctor Osler who are sure we've got to wear out and die sooner or later and why not sooner. And what if testosterone, raising my total vitality, making me burn the candle at both ends, does make me die sooner? I'd rather live not so long, but with my total vitality on a high sprocket, than drag along at a lower and lower level of living, saving myself till I'd pass out at last, a drooling dotard at ninety. It's only a little longer prime of life I'm after.

So I'll try fortifying my aging tissues according to the prescription of Herman Bundesen, according to his hunch that the male hormone may super-charge them just as chemicals renew worn-out soil.

CHAPTER TWENTY-FOUR

I KNOW I'm walking on very thin ice, trying to tell of another possible promise of testosterone to prop up the sagging lives of aging men. It's the grave question of the good the male hormone may do for men with prostate trouble, men who suffer those sad urinary miseries that are due, not to infection or cancer of the prostate gland, but to the simple enlargement of this organ so common in men past fifty. It makes life a burden for millions, a nightmare for many; and it turns some men into tragic social outcasts, ammoniacal.

I know I'm on dangerous ground. There are many scientific reports, nearly unanimous,* that the pure male hormone gives a new lease on life to many men suffering the prostate trouble that's due to the gland's simple enlargement. Yet here I have a grave responsibility. It is plain that nothing could be more dangerous than the indiscriminate shooting, into men who are urinarily bothered, of testosterone by every medical Tom, Dick, and Harry. It would be even more perilous if millions of such victims without any medical advice would go to drugstores to buy methyl testosterone as it is now becoming more and more cheap and abundant in the form of pills you can take by mouth.

For the ills that beset this little prostate gland, over and

---

* One of the few adverse reports is that of distinguished urologist, Doctor Norris J. Heckel, *Journal of Urology*, 43:286, 1940. He finds no marked good effect of testosterone upon troubles due to simple enlargement of the prostate. "Why our clinical results were not as favorable as those which have been consistently reported by a majority of other investigators, we cannot explain," writes honest Doctor Heckel.

beyond its simple enlargement, are many and various and often deadly. It is estimated that ten per cent of all prostate trouble is due to cancer; and it is known that an early cancer may hide in a simple prostate enlargement; and you recall that Doctor Walter Kearns proved that testosterone, generally so harmless and good, may speed up the growth of prostate cancer when it has already started.

So there is only one safe course of action for men whose lives are made miserable by *any* kind of prostate trouble— *and that's examination and treatment by a skilled urologist.*

This danger of the wild general use of methyl testosterone pills was made vividly clear to me by Doctor Walter Kearns. It quickly decided me against writing any dithyramb of hope that testosterone might hold out for such sad urinaceous old men, the vast majority of whom can, after all, be relieved by operations by expert urologists. Yet it's true that Walter Kearns himself had experimented cautiously with testosterone's effect upon certain men who suffered simple prostate enlargement. With the male hormone he treated men who refused operations, or weren't in physical shape to stand them, or men, said Kearns, "where the indications for surgical relief were not well defined."

Walter Kearns was not the man to be in a hurry to enrich himself by wielding his electric scalpel when there was a chance of helping any sufferer more cheaply, simply, and chemically. He had no *business* prejudice against the male hormone.

He found that testosterone did help a number of these unfortunate men suffering simple prostate enlargement. It did not decrease the size of their prostates. But it did notably increase the force and power of their formerly feeble and dribbling urination because of the new strength the male hormone gave them, so that the muscles of the bladder and abdomen could force the urine past the enlarged prostate; so that many of them were eased of their old gnawing pains and feeling of unrelieved fullness; so that many of them did not have to get up so often, and some of them did not have to get up any more at all in the night; so that they could sleep and wake up rested in the morning.

In the course of these cautious experiments, there was one observation about the general lives and the total condition of these particular older men, that hit Walter Kearns again and again. This was an upsurge of their feeling of well-being, of vigor, and their new bright outlook for tomorrow. They gave you a real grip now when they shook your hand, and they said they enjoyed their work again and were so happy at their new stamina.

And some who during their prostate trouble had been sexually impotent reported a resurge of their old sexual desire and power.

Yet Walter Kearns realized the almost universal medical skepticism about waning mental and physical strength of men past fifty; and as for rejuvenation, he knew that the doctors put the nastiest kind of a twist on that unfortunate word. It meant simply "to make young again." Well, if an old duffer of sixty, after testosterone, could work again with, more or less, the energy of forty, then he was young again, relatively, wasn't he? And if that same old duffer, after testosterone, could urinate like a younger man with a good strong stream, then to all intents and purposes you could call him, in that sense, younger. And if this same old man who had become completely impotent could now perform a modicum of sexual intercourse with autumnal enjoyment in a sedate and orderly manner, then you could say he had actually returned to a condition where he was, if not young, at least more than the man he used to be.

But here was the twist that many doctors, including certain high medical authorities, gave to that word rejuvenation. They hinted that testosterone claimed the transfiguration of old slippered pantaloons into the youthful splendor of some movie hero, like Clark Gable or Robert Taylor. Kearns realized that rejuvenation was the fightingest word in the entire medical lexicon.

I must grant that there was some justification for conservatism on the part of the good doctors regarding the possibility of testosterone's renewing older men's lives to any degree at all. These old codgers said they had a new feeling of well-being. Well-being indeed. That was the vaguest word in scientific language. It could mean anything or nothing, this "I feel so much better, Doc."

What medical doubters of this upstart, testosterone, had a right to demand, was a definite measurable proof of the male hormone's power to stoke up the total vitality—of old men's muscles and brains and nerves, and yes, of their sex lives that had become feeble or non-existent. Now the ogre that haunted all human experiments was that of suggestion. Old men got those shots and *imagined* they could prance about, and then they actually seemed to.

Now Walter Kearns had a stroke of inspiration. He knew that good doctors respect an objective demonstration. All right. Okay—he would put on a testosterone show where suggestion and imagination were ruled completely out of the picture.

The Male Hormone

CHAPTER TWENTY-FIVE

TAKE race horses; there you really had something. There you had the one animal among all God's creatures hand-picked for your testosterone experiment. In the whole animal kingdom, stamina, speed and power and fighting heart are best measured in this species. The performance of every race horse is precisely known. Its speed for the mile is clocked in split seconds. No ifs or buts or maybes. No imagination.

So now Doctor Walter Kearns left his clinic and the hospital and took his little satchel with gadgets and testosterone out to the race track. Here he would put testosterone to the toughest kind of trial. Our big, tough but genial Milwaukee doctor planted an enormous dose of five hundred and twenty-five milligrams of testosterone crystals under the aging hide of the famous but now hopelessly broken-down pacer, Holloway. Doctor Kearns knew that this tremendous dose would cause no explosion in our poor old nag, Holloway. It was scientifically established when you plant a big lot of male hormone under the skin of any animal or man, the body will only use up a tiny bit each day, a few milli-grams daily. It's a slick way of avoiding having to make constant injections.

Mind you, Holloway was past eighteen years old, and a gelding. That is, he had never known what it meant in life to have testicles. It is remarkable that horses are apparently less affected by being robbed of their sex glands than most other animals, yet it's true that their muscular systems and spirits are dampened by castration, no doubt of it. Among race-horses, stallions are the real immortals.

But for a gelding, this Holloway had been good. He had been one of the great pacers of the Grand Circuit. In his best days as a pacer, his record had been 2:05 for the mile. Then some years before this, to be exact, six years before the year 1941 of this experiment, Holloway had run away, three times around the track and had then fallen down. He was broken down after that, finished. He would start all right, but had no stamina or staying power at all. He was headed, poor old Holloway, for the glue factory.

So now in June, 1941, under the skin of this definitely emeritus racing gelding, Holloway, Walter Kearns shot those crystals of testosterone. He was plenty bold to expose his faith in testosterone to this toughest of all experiments. Its failure would make him the laughingstock of the sporting world; and don't worry, this test, if it flopped, wouldn't be long in grapevining through the hospital cloak rooms to his doctor friends, and would they kid him. Kearns, the rejuvenator! But one definition of a pioneer is a man who doesn't mind the sneers and laughter of the boys who stay home.

A few days after this momentous injection, if you'd been around the stables, you might have heard the horsemen say, looking at Holloway, "By God, that shot must be working!"

In Holloway, in point of scientific fact, the response to testosterone was remarkable. Promptly, this poor old has-been developed a spirit he'd never had in his whole nineteen years of living. He became anxious to exercise. Though only a gelding, and a broken-down and retired one at that, Holloway began to have terrific erections. He cavorted and curved his neck like a stallion and wanted to get out of his stable, and in every way was hell-bent to go to town. You can imagine Walter Kearns smiling. Since Holloway was only a horse, this could not possibly be construed, not by the most austerely critical superscientific doctor, as a mere effect of suggestion. It could hardly have been Holloway's imagination, connecting up that injection with his strange new feeling of elation.

If horses have thoughts, then the lives of geldings must be sad as they compare themselves to their stallion brothers. The geldings must have inferiority complexes in regard to stallions who are always winning and in other ways having a wonderful time.

Now day after day, Holloway not only felt like a million but looked better and better. His coat had in the past few years become very thin over his old face and various parts of his body. It began to return, getting thicker and thicker and shiny. He put on a fine coat all over. His muscles swelled and were firm. They harnessed him and began training him, and he was a whirlwind. Under testosterone, Holloway showed that an old horse can learn new tricks. His owners succeeded in training him to trot instead of using his natural gait of a pacer.

They wanted to make some money with Holloway and intended to enter him in the races as a green trotter since his former earnings as a pacer required his entry into the free-for-all class where competition would be too keen.

They needn't have worried about this new old Holloway. He'd gone 2:01 as a pacer. Then for six years he'd broken down so he couldn't do the mile in any kind of time whatever. Now, trotting as a green trotter, he was clocked at 2:07 for the mile!

In the middle of July, Holloway got another implantation of five hundred and twenty-five milligrams of testosterone by Doctor Walter Kearns. Now what he did in the sulky races as a green trotter could, again, hardly have been the effect of what the superscientific doctors call suggestion. Bright horse that he was, Holloway didn't have that vivid an imagination. That summer, in twenty-three heats, Holloway finished first in five, second in five, third in three, fourth in

six—and established an official record of 2:10 for the mile at
nineteen years of age.

Doctor Kearns gave him a third injection of testosterone
in August, but he didn't race after that due to a crack in one
hind hoof yet he was in wonderful condition. He showed
marked stud-like behavior. Yet he wasn't vicious. In October
his owners rewarded him. If horses do have thoughts and
are privately gloomy comparing their monkish lives sadly to
the love lives of stallions, then what now must have been
good old Holloway's exultation? They put him with a racing mare, and he mounted her and served her in the best stud-
horse style.

Now when good old Holloway was one with the mare,
fierce like any stallion, it could not have been suggestion, it
could not have been his imagination; it must have been those
injections of testosterone that made a totally different horse
of him. Again, being only a horse, he could not have known
that. But if a horse has thoughts, after this shattering fun
for the first time in all his nineteen years, he must have dimly
wondered, "Where has this been all my life?"

"In other words," wrote Doctor Walter Kearns, reporting
this fantastic demonstration in the *Journal of the American Veterinary Medical Association*, "Holloway was rejuvenated."

In the racing world this rejuvenation of worn-out geldings
and revigoration of geldings who at an early age have lost
their staying power, is spreading. Curiously, racing commis-
sions do not consider this an illegal hopping-up of race horses.
They do not object to the implantation of testosterone. They
announce, with a certain unction, that testosterone is not a
drug or a harmful stimulant, but that, in geldings, it replaces
a vital chemical, a natural constituent of their bodies, which
nature intended for them.

It was a great triumph for Doctor Walter Kearns. And
this stunning demonstration of testosterone's rejuvenation, I

must admit, made me feel more confident than ever in those experiments he had made upon those older men in whom testosterone had definitely, measurably increased the power of their muscles and nervous reflexes. It made me feel surer of that same effect, demonstrated by Doctor Guy Laroche of Paris, upon the blighted and down-at-heel lives of those seven sad old men. You remember.

Walter Kearns had shrewd common sense about what this beautiful experiment might mean for men in life's late afternoon and early evening. He didn't for a moment pretend that testosterone would turn old heavy-weight prize fighter, Harry Wills, into young Joe Louis. He'd never try to use the male hormone to bring a human middle-aged ex-sprinter to his old championship record for the hundred-yard dash. And, in his revigoration of men in mid-life, Kearns would be the first to warn against such quack slogans as "life begins at fifty or sixty or seventy-five."

And Walter Kearns had horse-sense counsel for older men who, after injections of testosterone propionate or pills of methyl testosterone by mouth, were elated to feel their sex drive and sex power upsurging.

"The man," said Walter Kearns, "who is well on in years, bald-headed, fat-bellied, thin-limbed, hard-of-hearing, out of breath when he walks upstairs, is never going to be a great lover again with any amount of testosterone."

CHAPTER TWENTY-SIX

THE MALE hormone is now ready for the trial of its possible power to extend the prime of life of men. In mid-life many a strong man becomes dismayed at an insidious sapping of his vitality when he should be at the top of his living and working stride. Some men come back, spontaneously, to vigor from this crisis that somewhat resembles the change of life of women. Then they may live to a lusty old age. Others, plagued by mysterious ills and gloomy, crumble into a premature senility. There's now the possibility of a new lease on life for countless men burnt out, as the saying goes, between the ages of fifty and seventy-five—*provided their doctors determine them to be suffering a serious hunger for the male hormone.*

This is the possible power and hope of testosterone.

This gleam of hope was hinted by Doctor August A. Werner, of the medical faculty of St. Louis University, in the *Journal of the American Medical Association* in 1939, though in his momentous little paper he did not state all of testosterone's possible implications. Doctor Werner did paint pretty clearly, though, the picture of this sapping of the total vitality of men in life's mid-passage. Following previous medical writers, he called it the climacteric, the male climacteric, just as it's called the female climacteric among women at the time of their change of life.

Doctor Werner tied this climacteric of men right up to the waning of the working of their sex glands; and he stated (what it takes no doctor to know) that the decline of sex function is not limited to women but is also the heritage of all men. Here the *Journal of the American Medical Association*, the most authoritative of our medical publications, opened the door to the scientific testing of the new male hormone to determine if it could bring about a resurge of the total vitality of men in their critical age when the fires of their lives just begin to burn lower. For this was what the highest hormone-hunting authorities demanded: that testosterone should only be used, and can only be *rationally* used, for men who have testicular deficiency, who are what's technically called "hypo-gonadal."

Very well, all men (with no formidable exception) become hypo-gonads around their fifties, some earlier, some later.

It is not necessary for them to be physically robbed of their testicles to be hypo-gonadal. Total vitality, we've seen over and over, is tied up to sexual vigor. And, losing their youth gradually, it is evident that all men suffer a slow, chemical castration that takes place invisibly with the passage of years. We've seen the brutal results of that disaster in those broken men who have lost their testicles by disease or accident. Now Doctor Werner, in his scientific report in the *Journal of the American Medical Association*, outlined the more subtle enfeeblement that accompanies the usually slow ebbing of the power of the testicles of men to produce the natural male hormone.

"Probably," wrote Doctor Werner, "a greater number of men than women pass through the climacteric without evident disturbance."

But then he uttered a warning that such a notion might be erroneous. After all, in women, the change of life has a visible sign—the stopping of their menstruation.

"Again," wrote Doctor Werner, "because of the prevalent belief that men do not have a climacteric period (which has been based on the cessation of menstruation in women) the condition has probably been overlooked or ignored in men."

Doctor Werner did not mince words, but tied their change of life right up to their waning of sexual vigor. He admitted that there were some wonderful old men (not living near fire-houses, and this is my own comment) who have become authentic fathers at eighty or over. But this fact, said Doctor Werner, doesn't change the evidence that many men show a beginning decline of sexual vigor at about fifty years of age.

Then, in his own properly cautious scientific manner, Doctor Werner went off the deep end for testosterone. "And during this period in life they (the men) have the typical climacteric syndrome which is mitigated by treatment with male sex hormones."

Syndrome is the fancy medical word from the Greek for a condition that doctors don't yet quite dare to call a definite disease. It is a set of symptoms which occur together, the sum of signs of any morbid state. Morbid state meaning a state of sickness.

What then was the condition of these men around the age of fifty in whom their sexual fires (by their own sad admission when they visited their doctors) were burning lower and lower?

Their bad condition was nervous; it was an upset blood circulation; it was general. As their sex drive waned, they began to feel a curious nervous tension and a definite instability of their emotions. They became irritable, and over nothing. They were easy to aggravate. They became moody, and the slightest mishaps might send them into jitters and nervous tailspins. Their memories went haywire; and when, in responsible positions, they tried to concentrate, they woolgathered. About business or any work or any prospect of their old fun, they tended now to say, "To hell with it." They didn't care. They wanted to be left alone. Over nothing they might burst out crying. They were likely to look on the dark side of professional or business problems that they used to take in their stride. At night they might fall asleep promptly but then come broad awake after a couple of hours and spend most of the night in crazy flights of thought and silly worries. They were ashamed of signs of what women suffer in their own change of life: these slipping men might have hot flashes so they'd want to rush out of the room into the open air; and they then might have to change their clothes because of drenching sweats that followed. Their minds, formerly alert, grew fuzzy and foggy. They couldn't make what used to be the easiest decisions.

They were losing their grip.

Doctor Werner reported a couple of typical cases in detail. The breakdown and the sadness and the sapping of the total vitality of these slipping men was very like the fate of the broken men who'd been physically robbed of their testicles, only the process was more subtle and insidious.

And Doctor Werner reported that injections of testosterone brought these men back to strength and hope and vigorous new life.

He was properly cagey in his conclusions. "It is evident," he wrote, "that some men develop a typical climacteric syndrome at about the age of fifty. It is reasonable to believe," wrote Doctor Werner, "that with decline of gonadal (testicle) function this should occur in men."

This was in 1939, and other conservative hints of this new revigorating power of testosterone came in scientific publications from France and England; and by the medical grapevine, the news began to spread of what testosterone accomplished for men's total vigor. It was, in its still obscure way, a little like insulin saving doomed diabetics; it might not be life-saving, but who could say, if testosterone became abundant and cheap enough and if it turned out to be as safe as it seemed to be, what it might promise for the prime of life of millions of slipping men?

It is no wonder that our medical authorities felt their responsibility and got set to shore up the dikes of the absolutely necessary medical conservatism against the flood of demand for this elixir—that awful word, that frightful thought of an elixir—that now might be expected to come from these millions of men who were not what they used to be.

And our medical authorities were still more worried about the testosterone manufacturers, and they didn't have to wait long for their worst forebodings to be justified. In this very year of 1939 a handsome pamphlet was circulated to the physicians of America. It was entitled "The Lure of the Land of Bimini." It was written (and not ghosted either, mind you) by Mr. Elmer H. Bobst, who was then President of the excellent pharmaceutical firm of Roche-Organon, Inc. This reputable house, along with Ciba, Inc., and Schering, Inc., had the rights of manufacture of testosterone. These houses had the expert chemists who were now planning large-scale production of the pure male hormone, that was powerful, invariable in its chemical composition and completely authentic.

Though the brands bore different names, they were all exactly the same testosterone.

Now, faced with a vision of what testosterone might do for millions of slipping men, Elmer Bobst didn't broadcast this terrific news to the public. Indeed, when you remember that Chemists Ružička and Butenandt were about to be offered the Nobel Prize for testosterone (the Nazis later forced Butenandt to decline it) it is remarkable how this hopeful news was kept out of the newspapers, popular magazines and off the airwaves. But Elmer Bobst was afire to tell the news to the men he thought should know it, to the doctors, and Elmer could write like a breeze, and now he went to town.

Before giving you the gist of his remarkable essay, I wish here to state that, in the medical uproar that followed it, I

definitely take the side of Elmer. Maybe in his poetic furor
he did draw a bit of a long bow, yet doctors are, after all,
only human beings like the rest of us. They are not scientific
calculating machines or mechanical robots in their art of healing. And it was Elmer's idea, as the great medical publicist
that he is, to begin his fine piece of prose by a twang on their
heart strings, an appeal to their emotions.

After all, your average doctor, as well as we mere lay people, wants to live as long and as strong as modern science
will let him. . . .

So now Elmer Bobst told the embattled physicians of
America, hard put to it to do a single damned thing for millions of men who were not what they used to be, sexually,
physically, or mentally, about a possible promise of testosterone. He didn't give them its structural chemical formula of
the keto-steroid that it is, scientifically. He began, "Dear
Doctor": and then he recounted the legend of good old
Ponce de Leon.

Ponce, said Elmer, had begun life as a fine-looking lad,
with a splendid physique and possessed of a daring personality. (*Cojones!*) His adventuresome spirit forced him at an
early age to take a hand in the Moorish Wars; and when he
was only thirty-three, it led him again to persuade Columbus
to take him along on his second trip to the new world. Then
as Ponce settled down to the rather soft and engaging life
of the Governor of Puerto Rico, the first shadow of old age
started to fall across his pathway. As Ponce de Leon's vigor
began to wane, wrote Elmer, the Indian legends about the
Land of Bimini and its wonderful spring of waters with their
marvelous curative powers intrigued him more and more.

When Ponce de Leon began his quest of the youth-restor-
ing waters, he was just about fifty years of age.

And right here, Elmer Bobst faded from poor old Ponce
into the misery of the slipping of men of middle-life today.
"Yes," he wrote, "just about the period of a man's life when

the downhill journey becomes significant. Is it due to the rapid decrease of the male sex hormone secretion at middle life? More and more physiologists and endocrinologists are coming to that conclusion."

Now, mind you, Elmer Bobst's accuracy in his little poem to the doctors can hardly be challenged, either in regard to the history of poor old Ponce de Leon, or to the scientific action of the male hormone, the waning of which helps to make men grow old too soon.

He might have been reasonably criticized by the medical authorities who are watch dogs against rank-and-file medical gullibility if he had dropped so much as a hint that if old Ponce de Leon had only had a few shots of testosterone when he got to the Land of Bimini, he would then have rared up, distended his nostrils, snorted, and proceeded to make all the Indian maidens of that land of the blue Caribbean.

But Elmer Bobst hinted no such quackish claims, nor did he imply them.

He simply drew the parallel between the change of life of women and the male climacteric in men and said that scientific study was leading rather definitely to the conclusion that the proper administration of testosterone propionate could play the same replacement role in the male climacteric that female hormones already played in the female change of life.

He suggested the *experimental* use of testosterone (giving it the Roche-Organon trade name) for "combatting the annoying symptoms of the male climacteric."

That was all.

Now hell broke loose upon the head of poor Elmer. The *Journal of the American Medical Association*, calling him by name, stated in its Current Comment that "this flamboyant exploitation obviously presupposes an extraordinary ignorance on the part of the physician."

And the American Medical Association's Council on Pharmacy and Chemistry, turning thumbs down on recognition of testosterone, remarked that it appeared that "many pharmaceutical firms would have one believe that in the ampoule of testosterone propionate lies the Fountain of Youth," and that really the few reports in the literature of attempted rejuvenation (that fighting word again) were not at all promising.

And if testosterone did have experimental promise to relieve the annoying symptoms of the male climacteric, so what? "The male climacteric," so the Medical Association's *Handbook on Glandular Physiology and Therapy* stated in 1942, ". . . is a relatively rare condition."

I wonder exactly how the good doctor who wrote this knew how rare the male climacteric really was? Upon how large a sample of middle-aged men had he tried the soundly scientific therapeutic test by the pure male hormone? But perhaps when you are an official authority you do not have to cite your documents. Not all of them.

The medical authorities were really a bit rough on Elmer Bobst. He is one of the kindest men I have ever known. He is of that finest American type, self-made, not spoon-fed or synthetic, who had home-studied to become a pharmacist; starting as a pharmaceutical salesman he'd taken hold of the nearly defunct American branch of the Swiss chemical house of Hoffmann-LaRoche, built it into one of the most powerful pharmaceutical chemical houses in America, doing a public health service as one of the biggest producers of chemically pure vitamins and hormones, a firm famous for its kindness to the thousands of men and women who worked for it. And this was Elmer's simple yen in writing poetically and emotionally about testosterone: he wanted the doctors to try it.

He wanted every last slipping-downhill, hormone-hungry man in America to have a hope for new total vitality if there was a chance that testosterone would help him to get it. He knew that only by a great demand for the pure male hormone could he, Elmer (and the other firms of Ciba and Schering), reach that mass production of testosterone that might finally put it within the reach of everybody. I'll never forget him as he sat one afternoon, big and calm and gray-eyed and smiling in the office of Donald M. Nelson where we were discussing the possible vitaminization of industrial workers to increase their war production.

I mentioned the old men and 4-F's who were building the boats for Henry J. Kaiser. "How about giving those old fellows daily pills of methyl testosterone, Elmer," I asked him.

His gray eyes gleamed. "It would be wonderful to *try* it, as an experiment," he said.

Since Elmer's spanking by the American Medical Association in 1939, the years have gone by. Here it is 1945, and it is no longer so certain that Elmer was wrong in recommending that the doctors try out testosterone for the annoyances (this is a nice mild word) that slipping men experience around and after the age of fifty.

Doctor August A. Werner, who by now had tested the power of the pure male hormone upon a large number of older men, read a report on its invigorating action before the annual meeting of the American Medical Association in 1944. It seemed not to be so sure that the male climacteric was a rare condition.

"Probably a greater number of men than women pass through the climacteric without evident disturbance," said Doctor Werner. "However, this inference may be based upon the fact that knowledge of the occurrence of this syndrome in men is of very recent date, and the condition possibly has been generally overlooked or ignored."

In his report of fifty-four carefully studied cases, Doctor Werner testified to testosterone's revigorating power. Among these slipping men testosterone renewed their physical energy and their mental sharpness and their courage. They slept well again, and their hot flashes and sweating vanished. Their muscle power resurged and their fatigue grew less; and once more they didn't mind tomorrow.

What about them, sexually? Ninety per cent of Doctor Werner's patients had come to him with complaints of their loss of sexual power, even though, curiously, some of them still had the desire which made their loss the more sad. In 1943, the year before this A.M.A. speech, Doctor Werner in a scientific paper had discussed testosterone's power to give aging men a new sexual lease on life. Apparently this passionate effect of testosterone was frequent among men who, though they might want their wives or sweethearts, could no longer maintain an erection.

"Occasionally," wrote Doctor Werner, "a patient is found who, when relieved of his symptoms, is disappointed because potency has not been restored to his satisfaction."

Occasionally.

This, of course, was the thinnest of ice for testosterone. This was medical dynamite. This, that happened to good old Holloway, was maybe not desirable for men.

"It might be well to add a word of caution on this point," said Doctor Werner. "It is questionable whether androgens (testosterone) should be administered to promote potency; at least, the return of potency should not be promised to the patient."

In his address to the doctors in 1944, Doctor Werner made this warning even stronger. "Testosterone should not be given," he said, "for the purpose of stimulating potency."

Although, mind you, it was the loss of their potency that in the great majority of men first announced their climacteric, and it was of this loss that most of them first came complaining.

"While it (the stimulation of potency) occurs in some patients, this result cannot be promised," said Doctor Werner, "and it is perhaps better for older men if this phase of the reaction does not result."

Why?

Being only a reporter, and not a doctor of medicine, I'm at a loss to say, nor have I found an authoritative medical pronouncement, about just how old a man should be before he is forbidden a return of a modest amount of sexual happiness.

However, this much may be said: I've talked to many investigators who are observing testosterone's power to lift the total vitality of many slipping men, restoring their muscular vigor, their nervous stability, their mental verve and clearness, and their stamina and their old calmness. Among these men, when they do experience it, there is no serious complaint at their upsurge, sexually.

In fact, most of them think it fine.

Hormone hunters are finding, so precise is the action of the pure chemical male hormone, that they can dose it so that general vitality and increased mental and physical power can be brought up on a higher step without the patients' having the desire to prance about like our old horse, Holloway. There are gradations. It's not a choice between becoming a Don Juan or remaining a dribbling old human vestige.

Perhaps this grave question should be investigated by a research committee of eminent and authoritative physicians. With due delicacy and discretion (what a research problem!) they might be able to determine the approximate age at which slipping middle-aged men could still be given doses of testosterone that would restore them to a modest, decorous, and orderly sexuality—without its being detrimental to their physique or their morals.

As the years have gone by, Elmer Bobst really seems pretty nearly to have hit the scientific bull's-eye in recommending that testosterone should be *experimentally* tried out by physicians, yes, the rank and file of doctors who, after all, are human, and who would be happy if they could have a weapon to return (somewhat) the vigor of slipping middle-aged men, to put them back into vigorous work and production and to prolong (who knows how much?) the prime of their lives.

Doctor August A. Werner's experience of testosterone's power against the male climacteric had been far from unique during the past five years.

Doctor H. R. Donald, of Manchester, England, brought testosterone to the rescue of fifty men in the middle and older ages of life. He found that their folding up, their losing their grip because of male hormone hunger, might steal upon men at any time between the ages of forty-two and seventy-six. He was hard-boiled about his experimenting. Lacking evidence of organic trouble with their testicles, he tried them out first with mock injections containing none of the male hormone. Nothing doing.

Then shots of testosterone produced a soaring of the total vitality of these men who had been on the downgrade, physically and mentally.

Doctor R. V. Day of Los Angeles treated one hundred and twenty-six mid-life men with the pure male hormone. They were suffering the depressed energy and spirits, the nervous exhaustion and debility so frequent in the middle and older years of life. He remarked upon the vastly increased power of synthetic testosterone, compared to the old impure gland extracts that for years had given the use of any male hormone preparation the medical black eye because of their inactivity.

Doctor Robert J. Douglas, of Muskegon, Michigan, raised the total vitality of fifty-eight aging men with testosterone and was pleasantly surprised at the way they came out of that lethargy and lack of hope for tomorrow that haunts so many men in their middle ages.

Doctor Charles W. Dunn, the veteran hormone hunter from Philadelphia, had for years deplored the insidious collapse of vigorous and enterprising men whose youthful energy had brought them to high positions in their businesses and professions. He has observed a series of thirty-five of these slipping men renewed in physical and mental power by the vital chemical testosterone.

Doctor Walter Kearns (the rejuvenator of Holloway) has witnessed the testosterone revigoration of more than fifty men whose hormone hunger had sent them downgrade prematurely toward the old age shadows. And Doctor Thomas H. McGavack, of New York City, reported how the male hormone relieved middle-aged men of pains over their hearts, the so-called pseudo-angina pectoris, and how it increased their vigor.

Numerous other scientific reports combine to document more than six hundred cases demonstrating the power of the pure male hormone to boost the total vitality of men past fifty. And what Elmer Bobst should demand in his kindly way (he was only annoyed briefly when they roughed him about the Land of Bimini) is the publication of the records to the contrary about testosterone. What he should ask the high medical authorities to publish are the authenticated reports of cases in which a male hormone hunger has definitely been demonstrated, in which testosterone does *not* give a lift to the total vitality of the men past fifty. There must be many such negative cases. Nothing is perfect. But the negative cases must not be phonies, must not be cases where a man's total vitality is sapped by some other actual disease condition and where testosterone could do no good at all.

And now, as Doctor S. Charles Freed has claimed it to be, is the male climacteric really a rare condition? Who knows? No dragnet has ever been drawn through any part of the male population of men past fifty; male hormone hunger—though it saps vitality—is in no sense yet a public health problem, a public health problem as of today being only whether any man or woman or child is alive at all or dead as a smelt. Public health does not yet deal with total vitality. No, nobody knows the extent of the need for testosterone of the men on the shady side of life's afternoon.

Doctors W. R. Mead and Robert Stith, of Florence, South Carolina, say that any doctor who will question a group of male patients between fifty and sixty-five will find a very large proportion of them worried and anxious about some ill-defined complaints which, while not adding up to actually disabling illness, nevertheless have gone a long way toward disturbing the former joy of living. This is the smouldering of the hormone hunger. Here is the type of the slipping man, they say: beset from all sides by vague worries, facing a future seeming inevitably to be leading to some unknown but ever threatening catastrophe, uncertain whether failing memory and poor power of concentration portend a mental crack-up, humiliated by apparently failing sex function.

This is their picture of the male climacteric.

Is it any wonder, they ask, that such men lose their zest for life? And it's only a step from that to the craziness of involutional melancholia, where the man spends much time in the contemplation of self-destruction. We all know of those apparently causeless suicides after fifty. . . . Of course, say Doctors Mead and Stith, such dramatic psychic changes are not frequent, but an appreciable loss of aggressiveness and a diminution of creative energy can be recognized in almost every man at this time of life. These are the men for a trial of testosterone.

"We have used it extensively and shall continue to use it because it is in every way analogous to the estrones (female hormones for the woman's climacteric) of proven value," say those South Carolina doctors.

To overcome reluctance of physicians to test the pure male hormone on their under-par men patients past fifty, in whom they can find nothing organically wrong, there's now sound scientific method. This reluctance is based on the deeply ingrained prejudice that the effect of testosterone is mainly one of imagination or suggestion—most doctors not having heard of Walter Kearns' rejuvenation of good old Holloway. To counteract this prejudice there is now what is called the therapeutic test of the male hormone. You give injections of testosterone propionate or pills of methyl testosterone to the man you suspect of male hormone hunger. If a seeming upsurge of physical and mental vigor takes place, granted, it may be purely imagination. So, *with his not knowing it,* you switch the man to blank injections or mock pills containing none of the vital chemical at all. If the man's troubles are actually due to male hormone hunger, then his evil symptoms will soon return, only to vanish again promptly when real male hormone treatment is resumed.

It's this scientific therapeutic test (and not the possibly wild claims of enthusiasts or the arbitrary negative ukases from medical authorities) that is going to uncover the extent and degree of the hormone hunger gnawing at men over fifty. Methyl testosterone that's taken in the form of pills by mouth has all the power of the testosterone propionate that's given by intramuscular injections; it can be taken by mouth daily indefinitely, and any digestive upset from it is extremely rare. The only difference between these two forms of testosterone is that you have to take roughly four times more of methyl testosterone—milligram for milligram—by mouth than you have to take of testosterone propionate by injection.

And it's far more convenient to take the pills than to make three visits a week to wait for a shot in the doctor's office. As insulin and the B vitamins have already shown, the growing demand for testosterone will soon bring it within reach of everybody. Then, in the form of a simple addition to their diets, we'll see what the vital chemical will do to extend the working life of millions of Americans.

We know how both the St. Louis Cardinals and St. Louis Browns have won championships, super-charged by vitamins. It would be interesting to watch the productive power of an industry or a professional group that would try a systematic supercharge with testosterone—of course under a good hormone hunter's supervision.

CHAPTER TWENTY-SEVEN

Now I'm fifty-four years old, and there's so much left to do. I've grown old much too quick and smart much too late, but at least I'm this much wiser than fifteen years ago, when I was sobbing a bit about not wanting to die. Then I said I didn't want to die because there were so many birds left that I didn't know the songs of. And what a picayune reason for wanting to go on living. Now I've at least learned enough to know why I want to go on living as long as possible on the biggest possible sprocket of total vitality. There's so much left to see and to find out about and to write about, and it's going to take a long time to do it. And it's going to take a long time to become a decent human being.

Now I see a gleam of hope of science to help me extend the prime of my life. I do not say it is more than a glimmer. I feel that testosterone has already helped me. Of course the male hormone isn't the whole story. I'll watch my nutrition and go on supercharging myself with vitamins just to be on the safe side, since God has played the trick on us of putting not quite enough vitamins in our food, even on the best-balanced diet. And I'll keep up cross-cut sawing and chopping the winter's fireplace wood with Frank Van Duren, now that Al Meyer and old Deplidge are dead. I'll stick to long hard walking in the dunes and along Lake Michigan in the wind and rain and sun. All this—plus methyl testosterone.

Herman Bundesen hasn't been wrong about testosterone. You were right, good tough old pal, Herman, about their possibly putting a bit of new life into my aging body. Now for a long time there have been fewer of those hot flashes and sweats and no longer that curious feeling of inward tremulousness. You were on the beam, too, Herman, about what the male hormone might do for my courage. I remember so well how, in 1940, before testosterone, when my old boss, Phil Rose, retired, I felt scared and alone and afraid of my future. The day old Phil's telegram came I was as if paralyzed and went to bed and stayed there all afternoon, scared that my working life was over. And you remember, Herman, how when the medical big boys were out to get me on the one-day syphilis cure, and when they'd cut down my writing production because of the necessity of having to answer them, how I griped that night in our Academy at the Hotel Drake when you told me I should go with you to Washington to get more money to keep the test of our one-day treatment going.

"Don't you realize my writing job is in danger?" I snapped. "I've got to write. I've got to go on earning my living."

What an exhibition of self-pity!

That was before testosterone. That was a nice little symptom of my own male hormone hunger, of my stage of slipping, of losing my grip.

Now tell me to go anywhere, and job or no job, I'll go. Now I don't care a damn about tomorrow.

Now my confidence about tomorrow is surging again, and my knowledge runs strong that a new fight for a better stronger life for all mankind is just beginning. It's like getting up in the morning and stretching and feeling my muscles strong and saying good morning to a new truth-hunting sunrise. Now at fifty-four it seems as if I've only just begun to write and that the best stories of the death fighters are waiting to be told and that I'm one of the boys to tell them. It is going to be tough hunting, but fun, to unearth the skeletons in scientific closets and find out and tell where the scientific bodies are buried and report the crimes of character assassination practiced by political doctors and follow keen on the trail of those strong-hearted hunters who are really out to make a less crippled and more totally vital mankind.

So, no different than a good diabetic child who knows that insulin every day makes the difference between living and dying, I'll be faithful and remember to take my twenty or thirty milligrams a day of testosterone. I'm not ashamed that it's no longer made to its old degree by my own aging body. It's chemical crutches. It's borrowed manhood. It's borrowed time. But, just the same, it's what makes bulls bulls. And, who knows, maybe tomorrow, they'll hit on a simple dietary chemical trick that will, to a degree, bring back the power of the glands that make my own natural male hormone.

Meanwhile I'll keep taking the methyl testosterone that now gives me the total vitality to go on working and waiting for such a not impossible discovery. Here's hoping.

BIBLIOGRAPHY

BIBLIOGRAPHY

The following is a list of original scientific publications which the interested reader may wish to consult.

I

Biochemistry and Physiology of Male Hormone

(1) W. C. Allee, N. E. Collias and C. Z. Lutherman: Modification of the social order in flocks of hens by the injection of testosterone propionate, *Physiol. Zoöl.*, 12:412, 1939.

(2) H. H. Beard and E. J. Jacob: Creatine-creatinine metabolism and the hormones, III. Effect of parenteral injection of creatine and creatinine with the sex hormones upon creatine-creatinine excretion in normal animals, *Endocrinology*, 26:1064, 1940.

(3) A. Butenandt: Über die Chemie der Sexual Hormons, *Ztschr. f. Angew. Chem.*, 44:905, 1931.

(4) A. Butenandt, H. Dannenbaum, G. Hanisch and H. Kudszus: Ueber Dehydroandrosterone, *Ztschr. f. Physiol. Chem.*, 237:57, 1935.

(5) A. Butenandt and H. Kudszus: Ueber Androstendion einen hochwirksamen männlichen Prägungsstoff. Ein Beitrag zur Genese der Keimdrüsenhormone, *Ztschr. f. Physiol. Chem.*, 237:75, 1935.

(6) A. Butenandt, and G. Hanisch: Ueber Testosteron. Umwandlung des Dehydro-androsterons in Androstendiol und Testosteron; ein Weg zur Darstellung des Testosterons aus Cholesterin, *Ztschr. f. Physiol. Chem.*, 237:89, 1935.

(7) K. David, E. Dingemanse, J. Freud and E. Laqueur: Ueber krystallinisches maennliches Hormon aus Hoden (Testosteron), wirksamer als aus Harn oder aus Cholesterin be-

reitetes Androsteron, *Ztschr. f. Physiol. Chem.*, 233:281, 1935.

(8) J. Eidelsberg, M. Bruger and M. Lipkin: Some metabolic effects of testosterone implants, *J. Clin. Endocrinol.*, 2:329, 1942.

(9) T. F. Gallagher and F. C. Koch: The testicular hormone, *J. Biol. Chem.*, 84:495, 1929.

(10) J. B. Hamilton: Significance of sex hormones in tanning of the skin of women, *Proc. Soc. Exper. Biol. & Med.*, 40:502, 1939.

(11) J. B. Hamilton and G. Hubert: Photographic nature of tanning of the human skin as shown by studies of male hormone therapy, *Science*, 88:481, 1938.

(12) R. G. Hoskins: Relation of androgens to kidney function, *J. Clin. Endocrinol.*, 3:111, 1943.

(13) W. M. Kearns: Testosterone pellet implantation in the gelding, *J. Am. Vet. M. A.*, 100:197, 1942.

(14) Allan T. Kenyon, *et al.*: A comparative study of the metabolic effects of testosterone propionate in normal men and women and in eunuchoidism, *Endocrinology*, 26:26, 1940.

(15) Allan T. Kenyon, *et al.*: The effect of testosterone propionate on nitrogen, electrolyte, water and energy metabolism in eunuchoidism, *Endocrinology*, 23:135, 1938.

(16) F. C. Koch: The biochemistry and physiological significance of the male sex hormones, *J. Urol.*, 35:382, 1936.

(17) F. C. Koch: The chemistry and biology of male sex hormones, *Bull. New York Acad. Med.*, 14:655, 1938.

(18) F. C. Koch: Chemistry of hormones. *Cold Spring Harbor Symposia on Quantitative Biology*, 10:61, 1942.

(19) F. C. Koch: The male sex hormones, *Physiol. Rev.*, 17:153, 1937.

(20) F. C. Koch: Recent advances in the field of androgens, *Cold Spring Harbor Symposia on Quantitative Biology*, 5:34, 1937.

(21) V. Korenchevsky and M. A. Ross: Kidneys and sex hormones, *Brit. M. J.*, 1:645, 1940.

(22) E. P. McCullagh and R. Jones: Effects of androgens on the blood count of men, *J. Clin. Endocrinol.*, 2:243, 1942.

(23) E. P. McCullagh and F. J. McGurl: Effects of testosterone propionate on epiphyseal closure, sodium and chloride balance and on sperm counts, *Endocrinology*, 26:377, 1940.

(24) E. P. McCullagh and H. R. Rossmiller: Methyl testosterone, I. Androgenic effects; II. Calorogenic activity; III. Body weight and growth, *J. Clin. Endocrinol.*, 1:496, 503, 507, 1941.

(25) L. C. McGee: The effect of the injection of a lipoid fraction of bull testicle in capons, *Proc. Inst. Med.*, 6:242, 1927.

(26) C. R. Moore: Gonadotropic substances and male hormone effects in the organism, *J. Urol.*, 42:1251, 1939.

(27) G. J. Newerla: The history of the discovery and isolation of the male hormone, *New England J. Med.*, 228:39, 1943.

(28) G. N. Papanicolaou and E. A. Falk: General muscular hypertrophy induced by androgenic hormone, *Science*, 87:238, 1938.

(29) L. Ružička, A. Wettstein und H. Kaegi: Sexualhormone VIII Darstellung von Testosteron unter Anwendung gemischter Ester, *Helv. Chim. Acta*, 18:1478, 1935.

(30) H. Selye: The effect of testosterone on the kidney, *J. Urol.*, 42:637, 1939.

(31) G. W. Thorn and L. L. Engel: The effect of sex hormones on the renal excretion of electrolytes, *J. Exper. Med.*, 68:299, 1938.

(32) G. W. Thorn and G. A. Harrop: The "Sodium Retaining Effect" of the sex hormones, *Science*, 86:40, 1937.

(33) G. W. Thorn, K. R. Nelson and D. W. Thorn: A study of the mechanism of edema associated with menstruation, *Endocrinology*, 22:155, 1938.

(34) A Symposium: Glandular physiology and therapy, American Medical Association, 1942.

II

General Clinical Applications of Male Hormone

(1) H. Arndt: Zur Therapie extragenitaler Störungen mit Sexualhormonen, *Wien. med. Wchnschr.*, 89:222, 1939.

(2) R. V. Day: Male sex hormone therapy, *J. Urol.*, 41:210, 1939.

(3) C. W. Dunn: Male hormone therapy, *Pennsylvania M. J.*, 45:362, 1942.

(4) J. Eidelsberg: The male sex hormone, *M. Clin. North America*, 22:1537, 1938.

(5) J. Eidelsberg and E. A. Ornstein: Observations on the continued use of male sex hormone over long periods of time, *Endocrinology*, 26:46, 1940.

(6) J. B. Engle and R. MacBrayer: Impotence in the dog: Its treatment with male hormone substance, *J. Am. Vet. M. A.*, 158, Aug., 1940.

(7) C. L. Hoagland, R. E. Shank and H. Gilder: Effect of testosterone propionate and methyl testosterone on creatinuria in progressive muscular dystrophy, *Proc. Soc. Exper. Biol. & Med.*, 55:49, 1944.

(8) W. M. Kearns: The clinical application of testosterone, *J. A. M. A.*, 112:2255, 1939.

(9) W. M. Kearns: Pellet implantation of hormones in urology, *J. Urol.*, 47:587, 1942.

(10) W. M. Ketcham: The male sex hormone, *J. Missouri M. A.*, 36:427, 1939.

(11) G. Laroche, H. Simmonnet, E. Bompard and J. A. Huet: Appréciation par des Tests Quantitatifs des effets de l'hormone mâle chez les vieillards, *Bull. Acad. de méd. Paris*, 119:639, 1938.

(12) I. I. Lubowe: Treatment of impotence with synthetic male hormone (Testosterone propionate), *M. World*, 58:362, 1940.

(13) T. A. Rennie, S. A. Vest and J. E. Howard: The use of testosterone propionate in impotence, *South. M. J.*, 32:1004, 1939.

(14) W. O. Thompson and N. J. Heckel: Male sex hormone, clinical application, *J. A. M. A.*, 113:2124, 1939.

(15) H. H. Turner: Clinical use of the male sex hormone, *South. M. J.*, 33:818, 1940.

(16) H. H. Turner: The clinical use of synthetic male sex hormone, *Endocrinology*, 24:763, 1939.

(17) S. A. Vest and B. Barelare: Androgens and the treatment of testicular hypofunction, *Clinics*, 1:1216, 1943.

(18) Council on Pharmacy and Chemistry, A.M.A.: The present status of testosterone propionate: Three brands, Perandren, Oreton and Neo-Hombreol (Roche-Organon) not acceptable for N.N.R., *J. A. M. A.*, 112:1949, 1939.

(19) G. B. Lake: Endocrines and the general practitioner, *Illinois M. J.*, 77:162, 1940.

III

Male Hormone Treatment of Castrates and Eunuchoids

(1) J. Eidelsberg and I. Madoff: Effectiveness of methyl testosterone administered orally, *Am. J. M. Sc.*, 202:83, 1941.

(2) L. Feinier and T. Rothman: Study of a male castrate, *J. A. M. A.*, 113:2144, 1939.

(3) R. S. Finkler and G. M. Cohn: The oral administration of methyl testosterone in a male castrate, *J. Urol.*, 45:548, 1941.

(4) G. L. Foss: The oral application of methyl testosterone and its simplification of androgen therapy, *Brit. M. J.*, 2:11, 1939.

(5) J. B. Hamilton: Treatment of sexual underdevelopment with synthetic male hormone substance, *Endocrinology*, 21:649, 1937.

(6) J. E. Howard and S. A. Vest: Clinical experiments with male sex hormones; further observations on testosterone propionate in adult hypogonadism, and preliminary report on the implantation of testosterone, *Am. J. M. Sc.*, 198:823, 1939.

(7) W. M. Kearns: Oral therapy of testicular deficiency; methyl testosterone administered orally to patients with marked testicular deficiency, *J. Clin. Endocrinol.*, 1:126, 1941.

(8) E. P. McCullagh: Peroral use of methyl testosterone in testicular deficiency, *Cleveland Clin. Quart.*, 7:226, 1940.

(9) E. P. McCullagh: Treatment of testicular deficiency with testosterone propionate, *J. A. M. A.*, 112:1037, 1939.

(10) N. E. Miller, G. Hubert and J. B. Hamilton: Mental and behavioral changes following male hormone treatment of adult castration, hypogonadism and psychic impotence, *Proc. Soc. Exper. Biol. & Med.*, 38:538, 1938.

(11) J. P. Pratt: Personal note on methyl testosterone in hypogonadism, *J. Clin. Endocrinol.*, 2:460, 1942.

(12) T. R. Robie: Psycho-endocrinotherapy in personality disorders of eunuchoidism; successful results with propylene glycol testosterone applied regularly to lingual veins, *Dis. Nerv. System*, 4:42, 1943.

(13) E. Simonson, W. M. Kearns and N. Enzer: Effect of oral administration of methyl-testosterone on fatigue in eunuchoids and castrates, *Endocrinology*, 28:506, 1941.

(14) S. A. Vest and J. E. Howard: Clinical experiments with androgens, IV. A method of implantation of crystalline testosterone, *J. A. M. A.*, 113:1869, 1939.

(15) S. A. Vest and J. E. Howard: Clinical experiments with the use of male sex hormones; use of testosterone propionate in hypo-gonadism, *J. Urol.*, 40:154, 1938.

IV

Male Hormone in Cardiovascular Diseases

(1) S. B. Beaser and T. B. Massell: Therapeutic evaluation of testosterone in peripheral vascular disease, *New England J. Med.*, 227:43, 1942.

(2) R. W. Bonnell, C. P. Pritchett and T. E. Rardin: Treatment of angina pectoris and coronary artery disease with sex hormones, *Ohio State M. J.*, 37:554, 1941.

(3) E. A. Edwards, J. B. Hamilton, and S. Q. Duntley: Testosterone propionate as a therapeutic agent in patients with organic disease of the peripheral vessels; preliminary report, *New England J. Med.*, 220:865, 1939.

(4) L. Hamm: Testosterone propionate in the treatment of angina pectoris, *J. Clin. Endocrinol.*, 2:325, 1942.

(5) M. A. Lesser: The treatment of angina pectoris with testosterone propionate, *New England J. Med.*, 226:51, 1942.

(6) Idem. (Further Observations), 228:185-88, 1943.

(7) S. A. Levine and W. B. Likoff: The therapeutic value of testosterone propionate in angina pectoris, *New England J. Med.*, 229:770, 1943.

(8) T. H. McGavack: Angina-like pain; a manifestation of the male climacterium, *J. Clin. Endocrinol.*, 3:71, 1943.

(9) Edward J. McGrath and Louis G. Herrmann: Influence of estrogens on the peripheral vasomotor mechanism, *Ann. Surg.*, 120:607, 1944.

(10) T. C. Walker: Use of testosterone propionate and estrogenic substance in treatment of essential hypertension, angina pectoris and peripheral vascular disease, *J. Clin. Endocrinol.*, 2:560, 1942.

(11) H. Zurrow, G. Saland, C. Klein, and S. Goldman: The effect of testosterone propionate in the treatment of arteriosclerosis obliterans, *J. Lab. & Clin. Med.*, 28:269, 1942.

V

Male Hormone in Mental Disease

(1) H. S. Barahal: Testosterone in male involutional melancholia; preliminary report, *Psychiatric Quarterly*, 12:743, 1938.

(2) H. D. Cogswell and S. C. Davis: Post-traumatic psychoses in the aged. Treatment with sex hormones, *Am. J. Surg.*, 62:9, 1943.

(3) L. Danziger and H. R. Blank: Androgen therapy of agitated depressions in the male, *Med. Ann. Dist. Columbia*, 11:181, 1942.

(4) E. Davidoff and G. L. Goodstone: Use of testosterone propionate in treatment of involutional psychosis in the male, *Arch. Neurol. & Psychiat.*, 48:811, 1942.

(5) A. Guirdham: Treatment of mental disorders with the male sex hormone, *Brit. M. J.*, 1:10, 1940.

(6) G. Schmitz: Erfahrungen mit dem neuen synthetischen Testeshormon präparat "Perandren," *Deutsche med. Wchnschr.*, 63:230, 1937.

(7) H. B. Thomas and R. T. Hill: Testosterone propionate and the male climacteric, *Endocrinology*, 26:953, 1940.

(8) O. L. Weiss: Behandlung psychischer Alterserscheinungen bei Männern und Frauen mit synthetischem Testeshormon, *Deutsche med. Wchnschr.*, 65:261, 1939.

VI

Male Hormone in Prostatism

(1) I. G. Duncan: Our experience with testosterone in more than three hundred cases, *Memphis M. J.*, 18:52, 1943.

(2) N. J. Heckel: The influence of testosterone-propionate upon benign prostatic hypertrophy and spermatogenesis: A clinical and pathological study in the human, *J. Urol.*, 43:286, 1940.

(3) W. M. Kearns: Testosterone in the treatment of testicular deficiency and prostatic enlargement, *Wisconsin M. J.*, 40:927, 1941.

(4) W. F. Keller and W. M. Hull: Histopathological changes in the prostate following testosterone propionate therapy, *Urol. & Cutan. Rev.*, 44:18, 1940.

(5) E. Laqueur: Behandlung der Prostataphpertrophie mit männlichem Hormon (Hombreol) und experimentelle Begründung dieser Therapie, *Schweiz. med. Wchnschr.*, 64:1116, 1934.

(6) M. J. Markham: The clinical use of peroral methyl testosterone in benign prostatic hypertrophy, *Urol. & Cutan. Rev.*, 46:225, 1942.

(7) M. J. Markham: The clinical use of testosterone propionate in benign prostatic hypertrophy, *Urol. & Cutan. Rev.*, 45:35, 1941.

(8) M. Meltzer: Male hormone therapy of prostatic hypertrophy, *J.-Lancet*, 59:279, 1939.

(9) J. G. Strohm, Z. C. Edelson and G. H. Merryman: Clinical use of testosterone in the treatment of benign prostatic hypertrophy, *Urol. & Cutan. Rev.*, 42:510, 1938.

(10) A. Trasoff: The treatment of benign prostatic hypertrophy with testosterone propionate, *J. Lab. & Clin. Med.*, 25:377, 1940.

(11) Staff of Davis Hospital: Treatment of prostatic conditions, *South. Med. & Surg.*, 101:326-A, 1939.

VII

Male Hormone in Male Climacteric and Gonadal Insufficiency State

(1) H. R. Donald: Observations on the male climacteric, *Clin. J.*, 67:323, 1938.

(2) R. J. Douglas: The male climacteric: Its diagnosis and treatment, *J. Urol.*, 45:404, 1941.

(3) C. W. Dunn: Male hormone therapy of the male climacteric and the gonadal insufficiency state, *Delaware State M. J.*, 11:76, 1939.

(4) S. F. Goldman and Mark J. Markham: Clinical use of tes-

tosterone in the male climacteric, *J. Clin. Endocrinol.*, 2:237, 1942.

(5) C. P. Lamar: Clinical endocrinology of the male with especial reference to the male climacteric, *J. Florida M. A.*, 26:398, 1940.

(6) W. R. Mead and R. Stith: The male climacteric, *J. South Carolina M. A.*, 36:222, 1940.

(7) H. B. Thomas and R. T. Hill: Testosterone propionate and the male climacteric, *Endocrinology*, 26:953, 1940.

(8) A. A. Werner: The male climacteric, *J. A. M. A.*, 112:1441, 1939.

(9) A. A. Werner: The male climacteric: Additional observations of thirty-seven patients, *J. Urol.*, 49:872, 1943.

INDEX

INDEX